Best Foot Forward

Charles Albert Blatchford, aged about 47, some 20 years after he founded the firm that bears his name.

Best Foot Forward

CHAS. A. BLATCHFORD & SONS LTD. (ARTIFICIAL LIMB SPECIALISTS) 1890 – 1990

GORDON PHILLIPS

GRANTA EDITIONS

Picture Credits

Art Gallery of South Australia, 28, 29; *Basingstoke & North Hampshire Gazette*, 101, 103, 120; Blatchford family and Company archives, Frontispiece, 4, 8, 10, 18, 21, 22, 23, 39, 42, 50, 52, 53, 56, 61, 62, 64, 65, 66, 67, 68, 71, 73, 74, 76, 77, 78, 79, 80, 83, 91, 92, 96, 106, 107, 108, 110, 116, 118, 131; Clive and Philip Blatchford, 15; Dr Ian Fletcher, 48, 84; Graham Photography, 133; Greater London Record Office, 38; Guildhall Library, 35; Imperial War Museum, 47, 54, 60; G. Judge, 105; Alan and Joyce Matthews, 16, 19, 20; National Trust, 31; Gordon Phillips, 2, 26; Royal College of Surgeons, 27; Scott Publicity Services, 117, 119, 123, 128; Southwark Local Studies Library, 7, 9; Roy Thompson, 6; Times Newspapers, 29, 32, 41; Wellcome Institute for the History of Medicine, 27, 34, 36, 43, 72.

© Chas. A. Blatchford & Sons Ltd. 1990
First published 1990

ISBN 0 906782 48 1

Published by Granta Editions
47 Norfolk Street, Cambridge CB1 2LE
Granta Editions is an imprint of The Book Concern Ltd

Designed by Jim Reader
Design and production in association with
Book Production Consultants, Cambridge

Typeset by KeyStar, St Ives, Cambridge

Reproduced, printed and bound in Great Britain by
BPCC Hazell Books
Aylesbury, Bucks, England
Member of BPCC Ltd.

Contents

List of Illustrations

Foreword

by the Marquess of Anglesey

'By God, sir, I've lost my leg!' Thus is my great-great grandfather supposed to have exclaimed when, by almost the last shot fired in the Battle of Waterloo, a grape-shot shattered his right leg. He was riding beside Wellington at the time. That great man, the popular version of the incident has it, removes the telescope from his eye, considers the mangled limb, says 'By God, sir, so you have!' and resumes his scrutiny of the victorious field.

While a few hours later the saw (now in the National Army Museum) was at its amputating work, Lord Uxbridge (soon to be created Marquess of Anglesey) 'never', according to an A.D.C. 'moved or complained: no one even held his hand.' Within three weeks he was back in London. That he was a tough nut to crack is evidenced by his being alive and kicking (with one leg) at eighty-five!

One of the articulated artificial limbs which James Pott made for him the following year is displayed at Plas Newydd, his North Wales home, now owned by the National Trust. The history of that striking relic, like much else of absorbing interest, is told in this remarkable centenary volume by Gordon Phillips.

It is right that such an important milestone in the career of Charles A. Blatchford & Sons should be marked by a thoroughly scholarly and highly readable chronicle. After all, for a hundred years the Blatchfords (whose family history forms not the least intriguing section of the book) have been performing a service to the disabled which ranks high amongst the achievements of twentieth-century medicine.

Both as pure history and as a record of progress from the comparatively primitive prosthetic art (for it is no less than an art) of the end of the nineteenth century to its present high technological state, this book excels.

I am honoured to have been asked to write a foreword to so important and interesting a work and I commend it unreservedly to a readership which I hope will not be confined to specialists in the subject.

Anglesey

The Marquess of Anglesey,
Hon. D Litt., FSA, FRHistS,
FRSL

Family Tree

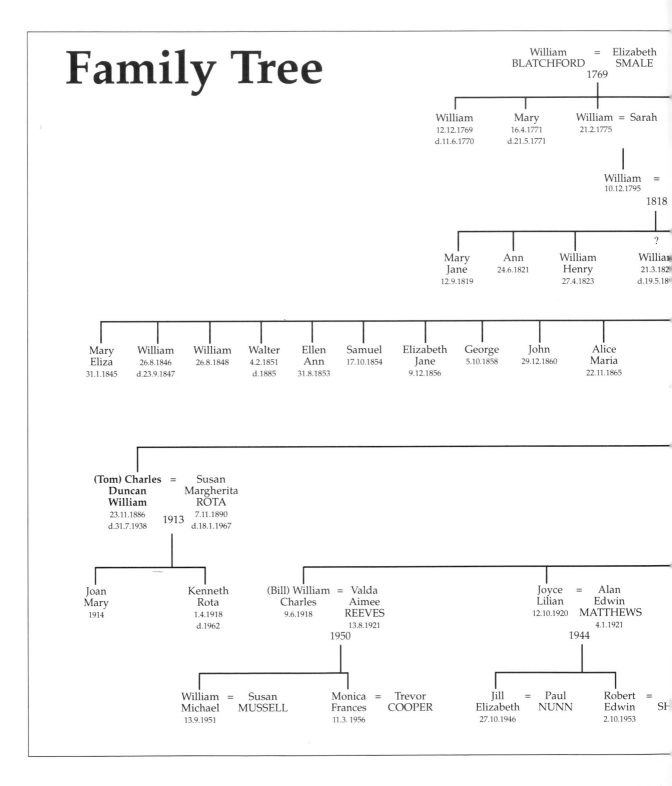

William BLATCHFORD = Elizabeth SMALE
1769

William
12.12.1769
d.11.6.1770

Mary
16.4.1771
d.21.5.1771

William = Sarah
21.2.1775

William =
10.12.1795
1818

?

Mary
Jane
12.9.1819

Ann
24.6.1821

William
Henry
27.4.1823

Willian
21.3.182
d.19.5.18

Mary
Eliza
31.1.1845

William
26.8.1846
d.23.9.1847

William
26.8.1848

Walter
4.2.1851
d.1885

Ellen
Ann
31.8.1853

Samuel
17.10.1854

Elizabeth
Jane
9.12.1856

George
5.10.1858

John
29.12.1860

Alice
Maria
22.11.1865

(Tom) Charles
**Duncan
William**
23.11.1886
d.31.7.1938
= Susan
Margherita
ROTA
7.11.1890
d.18.1.1967
1913

Joan
Mary
1914

Kenneth
Rota
1.4.1918
d.1962

(Bill) William
Charles
9.6.1918
= Valda
Aimee
REEVES
13.8.1921
1950

Joyce
Lilian
12.10.1920
= Alan
Edwin
MATTHEWS
4.1.1921
1944

William
Michael
13.9.1951
= Susan
MUSSELL

Monica
Frances
11.3. 1956
= Trevor
COOPER

Jill
Elizabeth
27.10.1946
= Paul
NUNN

Robert
Edwin
2.10.1953
= SH

viii

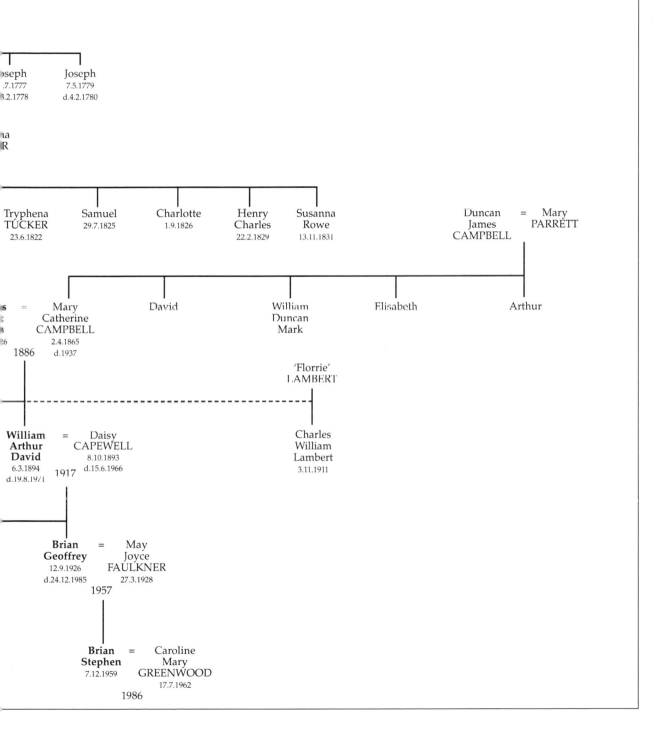

Joseph
.7.1777
3.2.1778

Joseph
7.5.1779
d.4.2.1780

na
R

Tryphena
TUCKER
23.6.1822

Samuel
29.7.1825

Charlotte
1.9.1826

Henry
Charles
22.2.1829

Susanna
Rowe
13.11.1831

Duncan
James
CAMPBELL

= Mary
PARRETT

s =

Mary
Catherine
CAMPBELL
2.4.1865
d.1937

David

William
Duncan
Mark

Elisabeth

Arthur

1886

'Florrie'
LAMBERT

**William
Arthur
David**
6.3.1894
d.19.8.1971

= Daisy
CAPEWELL
8.10.1893
d.15.6.1966

1917

Charles
William
Lambert
3.11.1911

**Brian
Geoffrey**
12.9.1926
d.24.12.1985

= May
Joyce
FAULKNER
27.3.1928

1957

**Brian
Stephen**
7.12.1959

= Caroline
Mary
GREENWOOD
17.7.1962

1986

Acknowledgements

A special note of gratitude is due to the Marquess of Anglesey, whose Foreword rekindles memories of the limb worn by his ancestor, possibly the most famous artificial leg of all time. Of enormous benefit were instructive discussions with Joyce Blatchford, Bill Blatchford and Alan and Joyce Matthews of the immediate family. Their recollections, anecdotes and personal insights give a tone and authority to the book. Bill Blatchford was able to draw upon a lifetime's knowledge of patent applications to vet the references to the company's list of innovations, and Michael Blatchford spent valuable time in compiling an exhaustive list of patents granted to Blatchfords. Assistance generously given, came from many other individuals, most notably: Tony Rainbird, whose detailed tabulations of company trading figures since 1925 kept the author on the straight and narrow; John Shorter, for an evaluation of early Blatchford and other design specifications; H. 'Tommy' Thompson, always ready to blend *bonhomie* with candour, and his thoughtful contributions were deeply appreciated. Then, Kenneth Chick provided both a narrative history of his forty years with Blatchfords and, in conversation, a zestful account of what life was like at the 'sharp end' of the industry, where patient, physician, prosthetist and finished product all met. Tony Naylor, along with David Peck, were others who spoke in like manner of how they 'lived this work'.

The springboard for a pilgrimage to trace the footsteps of Charles Albert Blatchford and visit the scenes of his upbringing was provided a decade ago by work done on the family history by Jean Wood, Pat Crawley and Michael Blatchford. This was complemented and amplified by Michael Wickes, a Devon-based professional genealogist, and the findings scrutinised and analysed by Alvine Rainbird, who then drew the family tree from sources provided. Kenneth Drouet brought our attention to his mother, Violet Drouet, who, more than seventy years after the happy day, was able to identify almost all the wedding group photographed after Tom Blatchford's marriage ceremony.

Sandra Bishop, Personnel Manager at Blatchfords, kindly circularised retired members of staff, seeking answers to a questionnaire provided by the author, and among those who replied, mention must be made of George Bourdon, George Sargeant, Norah Smith and William Sturge. What they had to say was not only constructive but enjoyable. A debt is due to others who offered either guidance or assistance: Ian Armstrong (Scott Publicity Services); Alane A. Blachford in the United

States; Clive and Philip Blatchford; Dr Ian Fletcher, for a guided tour of the Roehampton museum exhibits and matchless commentary; Ros Ham; Freddie James; David Linton; Peter Miller; Carol Morgan of the *Basingstoke & North Hampshire Gazette*; Godfrey New (who achieved minor miracles on one photographic image); Leonard N. Pardoe, senior partner at the firm of solicitors Arnold, Fookes, Chadwick, who signed over a collection of company legal papers untouched for more than half a century; Dr Robin Redhead, Senior Medical Officer at the Disablement Services Authority's headquarters at Roehampton; and Roy Thompson, without whose articles on the history of the tannery industry the aroma of the Victorian tannery workshops might have passed unnoticed – except to those living in Bermondsey.

Research without recourse to libraries and archives is unthinkable, and special help came from D.A. Armstrong, Records Officer at the Church Commissioners; Fiona Price at the Lambeth Archives Department; the staff of the Imperial War Museum, who broke speed records in the provision of photographs; Southwark Local History Library proferred maps, pamphlets, Census returns, directories and photographs; but rarely, if ever, has the author chanced upon a more pleasant group of people than those who look after visitors to the Library of the Wellcome Institute for the History of Medicine.

I cannot overstate my indebtedness to Stephanie Zarach of Book Production Consultants, whose contribution to this book far exceeded the bounds of natural duty. At times of despair, she was supportive, resourceful and caring. When the occasional section seemed to write itself she shared the sense of well being, but retained an immensely practical, sane and down-to-earth mien.

Stephen Blatchford commissioned the centenary history, gave it the necessary impetus and has presided over meetings of the subcommittee dedicated to its publication. His meticulous eye for detail has been invaluable and his interventions throughout have been apt, fair and forthright. Preparation and progress of this work could not have been possible without him, but faults in the text are the author's responsibility only.

Introduction

As achievements of scientific excellence, modern artificial limbs are near miracles of human ingenuity and represent the closest possible thing to perfect substitute faculties. Yet, perversely, their manufacture has not enjoyed a healthy share of space in the press. Coverage of this recondite arm of the caring services, even in the medical journals, has been patchy, often non-existent. Not until Chas. A. Blatchford & Sons Ltd. reached a well deserved century has there been a real effort to chronicle, through historical and anecdotal background, any history of private enterprise and design innovation in what is an admittedly, albeit unfairly, out of the way industry.

Charles Albert Blatchford was born into a society which largely confirms the persistent tendency we have of associating artificial limbs with horrific accidents and war. Now, worlds apart not so much in time as in technology, he would be intrigued to discover that the majority of limbs are supplied not for trauma, but as the result of benevolent surgery, made necessary by the consequences of ageing or various circulatory disorders. Such is the cyclical nature of history that whereas Victorian soldiers and seamen were relatively well set up for government-funded limb substitutes, the civilian halt and lame found little room for manoeuvre, unless they could fall back on private resources or a share-out from yesteryear's equivalent of BUPA, the Friendly Societies and charities.

Chas. grew into manhood and ran his own company in the Victorian equivalent of modern highly competitive tendering conditions, where money was the main criterion. It was not a question of whether the part could be replaced, but whether the cost could be afforded, and, in an open market, who was to provide it. The proverbial wheel has turned full circle with the re-introduction of competitive tendering.

For centuries the provision of a prosthesis was chiefly to conceal the loss of a limb, so while it may not meet universal approval, dovetailing a general history of artificial limbs into a single chapter has been an awesome task, but vital in setting the scene. Sample catalogues from a range of manufacturers, listing very much the same derivative products, survive in some libraries and archives. Primarily they focus on the Anglesey leg and other English patterns made upon it from upwards of a century, before the First World War tore asunder what had been a cottage industry and transformed it into international big business. Only then did parliamentarians become really involved, and the question of new limbs, wood vs. metal, became a matter for wide and incessant debate. Wood and leather are natural substances, in that they 'breathe', and self-confessedly Blatchfords was never at its best with metalwork. The company, however, has always been flexible enough to meet or even anticipate the demands of a more discriminating and articulate clientele, backed by the full weight of government spending.

During a talk at his old *alma mater*, St Edward's, Oxford, Brian Blatchford, grandson of the founder, said of design work, 'It is absolutely vital to be unafraid of seeking the unusual solution. Innovation is essential to the success of an engineering organisation'. The poet, Thomas Hood, is largely forgotten, but in the *New Monthly* magazine (1840) he extolled 'Miss Kilmansegg and Her Precious Leg':

But when it came to fitting the stump
With a proxy limb - then flatly and plump
She spoke in the spirit olden;
She couldn't - she shouldn't - she
wouldn't have wood
Nor a leg of cork, if she never stood,
And she swore an oath, or something as good,
The proxy limb should be golden.

Golden, yes, but I suspect she would have settled for an Endolite leg by Blatchfords. The interaction of engineering and the medical science of prosthetics, as embodied in the Endolite range of standard component parts, has lifted artificial limb technology into dimensions undreamt of by Chas. It has rewritten the rule book which ordained that an accurate imitation of the external form of the natural limb is incompatible with good function, and to attempt, for aesthetic reasons, to give every patient the same appliance, would only lead to disappointment. The Endolite system combines both, and as such is the present pinnacle of strong moves by the company over four decades to improve the functionality of the

leg by including a wide range of alternative control devices. In-house development at Blatchfords of strong, light alloys and plastics, plus hard wearing bearings and joints, brings the patient directly into the R&D environment, which is where Blatchfords believe they properly belong. The markedly British penchant for denigrating our own wares, while praising the virtues of, say, German artificial limbs, has happily suffered a rebuff in the refinements of Endolite, which allow amputees to walk at different speeds over uncertain terrain, while maintaining a normal looking gait; to run, cycle and scale the stiffest crags.

The family firm of Blatchfords has straddled a century which has witnessed examples both of mankind's most wilful excesses of lunatic maiming in the shape of two World Wars, and of the noblest, most selfless ideals of a health service for all, wherein the goal of prosthetic science is the total rehabilitation of the limbless human being. Patients are not allowed to resign themselves to a life of disability, and the striking dependence of the surgeon and patient upon the engineer and prosthetist helps determine the success with which the disabled can live full, active lives. Bearing in mind that some sixteen different types of amputations need to be covered, all load bearing with close body contact, most amputees will avow that 88 per cent of persons wearing modern limbs are perfectly satisfied that they can defy all the odds, step out in style and, hung heavy with headline clichés, enjoy a new lease of life.

When a firm has performed its proper function for a hundred years, its history must contain a good deal that is noteworthy, and the story of Blatchfords, from its stuttering start in 1890 as a back-street, almost bicycle-shed existence, unfolds as a tale rarely told. There is an element of speculation about the earlier years, but history without speculation can be very dull, and this is no dull recital. It is the success story of a private firm which has known its ups and downs, usually linked to government patronage, liberal in wartime and during the tenure of contracts; illiberal when they were lost. Family will-power and self-belief that exceptional design talent cannot be ignored has overcome stumbles along the way, and a burgeoning export market replicates the self-confidence of its founder who claimed 'exports' in his first advertisements. The influence of Chas., an East End boy, tough, resourceful and hungry for success, permeates this book. I salute him, just as amputees, these past 60 years or so since his death, salute his successors.

Ealing, March 1990.

CHAPTER ONE

Early Days

Grief, compounded by lack of opportunities for advancement at home in Zeal Monachorum, probably spurred William and Tryphena Blatchford, then both in their mid-twenties, to make the short journey to Exeter. From there, via the Great Western Railway, they would tackle the great unknown in the anonymity of narrow streets and squalid squares which made up the London of Charles Dickens. In doing so, they offer us a human dimension to what historians have seen as a massive exodus from the south-west of England to London and the colonies, consequent upon the collapse of the Exeter woollen and cloth-making industries and the decline of Devon tanneries. Behind the familiar picture-calendar façades of many similar Devon villages lie years of struggle for survival.

Both these young people were bred-in-the-bone Devonians, attuned to the slow pace of the changing seasons, and for a working-class couple in 1848 to exchange village life for the turmoil of a great city demanded some sort of traumatic upheaval. In the case of William, apparently a loner and – in the days of poor local communications – far from home, the decision may not have been too difficult, but Tryphena's roots ran deep and she seems to have been part of a large and cohesive family.

She would also have been responsible for the additional burden of a two-year-old daughter, Mary Eliza. They had just buried William, aged one, on 23 September 1847, and their distress is imaginable.

Zeal Monachorum was well and truly off the beaten track, and even today it is omitted from many guidebooks. The sort of place, in fact, where in the 1840s very little happened when the sun went down. It remains a picturesque, sleepy village in mid-Devon, with a twisting main street and attractive thatched cottages clustering on a hilltop by the fourteenth-century church of St Peter the Apostle. Some five hundred feet above sea level, it commands extensive views south over Dartmoor and looks northwards toward the gentler slopes of Exmoor.

First alluded to in AD 967, it was originally called Sale or Zele Monachorum. The latter part of its name is taken from ancient associations with the Benedictine monastery at Buckfast, to which estate it was added in 1016 by King Canute. Zeal is derived from *cella in monachorum*, the cell of the monks, part of the present church being a cell or outlier for the Buckfast monks. W. G. Hoskins, in his book *Devon*, first published in the 1950s, describes it as a 'small cob and thatch village in unfrequented country'. As befits a more

From Zeal Monachorum, Devon, the pathway led to Bermondsey. A street scene in Zeal very much as William Blatchford and Tryphena would have known it on their wedding day, half a century before this picture was taken.

leisured, expansive age, *White's Devon Directory* (1850) accords it more space, depicting a village and parish in Taw Vale, 8 miles WNW of Crediton, a self-contained community with a population of about six hundred. It ran to a wheelwright, a farming implement maker, a brace of carpenters and blacksmiths, two shops and a pub, the Golden Lion. Many of its members supplemented their income with a variety of second skills. It lacked piped water until 1897 but two manor houses added gloss to an essentially rural community.

Given a few minor adjustments, discernible only to a familiar eye, this would have been the village exactly as William Blatchford knew it. He is first identified in the Census of June 1841,

giving his age as 20 and living as an apprentice with two other employees at Wick, a farm run by William Walford or Wreford. His apprenticeship may have been slanted towards harness manufacture and repair, giving him a background in leather virtually from boyhood. Zeal Monachorum was part of a tanning and woollen area well into living memory, and it may not be too presumptuous to argue that William picked up the general principles of the trade and capitalised upon his early knowledge, working within the orbit of the Sanders family. The tannery yard, run by James Sanders, was a couple of miles to the south, in the 'small, decayed' market township of Bow, a characteristic 'street village' of the period, sitting astride the Crediton – Okehampton road. One of the witnesses to William's wedding, and by inference a close companion, was John Sanders, the young schoolmaster in Zeal as well as local Census enumerator.

Oak bark, for centuries the essential

ingredient in the production of tannin, had been plentiful, but agricultural progress and drainage improvement had drastically reduced the amount of land available for afforestation. To compensate for an increasing shortage of tannin material as well as of home-based hides, vegetable tannins and chemical compounds had to be imported. The insatiable demand at the same time for harness, saddlery and industrial leathers of every description caused prices to soar, to the detriment of numerous small tan yards. Scores of inland country tanneries went out of business, and in Devon alone it has been estimated that from 1847 onwards at least sixty tanneries shut down. Tanning was now enormously biased towards London, and it is inconceivable that even in a backwater like Bow, a small yard under threat of closure could not have known of the widespread advertising for skilled hands carried by the provincial press on behalf of London firms.

Having completed his apprenticeship and attained majority, William married Tryphena Tucker, 'both of full age', in the Zeal parish church on 30 June 1844. The date is critical, as we shall see. Most of the wedding details are known and can be amplified. Tryphena was a weaver by trade, baptised in Bow on 23 June 1822, and able to sign the register, whereas William, a labourer, born in Exeter, simply made his mark. Her father, also William, was present at the ceremony, with her mother, Elizabeth, and younger sisters Alice and Jane in attendance. Few girls today would thank their parents for the name Tryphena, but, quixotically, there was another Tryphena Tucker in the same tiny village, also working as a weaver but on the other side of the street, both of them in 'Zeal Town'. That it was very much a West Country name for girls is self-evident, and indeed Thomas Hardy's first cousin (and alleged mistress) was a Tryphena Sparks.

The critical point, however, is that there was no Blatchford *père* made known at the wedding. In normal circumstances the only conclusion to be drawn from this is either that he was illegitimate or that his father was dead. Also, as we have seen, William was illiterate. On the other hand a case can be made that he married without the involvement of a parent to sanction it, either because he had left home at an early age without any sort of schooling and against his parents' wishes, and therefore chose not to give their names, or he felt reluctant to ask them to undertake a difficult journey by road to what had all the potential for an explosive situation. William and Tryphena's first child, Mary Eliza, was baptised in Zeal on 31 January 1845, and any necessary conclusions are easily drawn.

The case for William's illegitimacy is shot through with doubt. Fortunately for genealogists, although Exeter is a venerable city containing a large number of small parishes, its pre-1837 records of 'hatches, matches and despatches' are superbly well indexed. Blatchford is an Old English name, derived from *blaec*, or black, and crops up frequently in the West Country so that contenders for William's ancestry dart in and out of the lists, especially in a period of high infant mortality. Robert Southey, the poet, said in 1799 that 'Exeter is ancient and stinks', and in the cholera epidemic of 1832 one in every 28 people was affected. Once a centre for industry, the vitality of urban life was on the wane in the middle of the nineteenth century, and notions of public works, sewage and sanitation were raw in the extreme, so that a scrutiny of baptisms and burials makes depressing reading. With this in mind, any probing of the past asks of the reader a willing suspension of disbelief. Even so, common sense and age comparisons do yield a tentative solution to his parentage. Inexplicably, William did an about turn for the 1871 Census return. Having given Exeter as his birthplace in 1851 and 1861, in middle-age he chose Okehampton,

William and Tryphena's wedding certificate.

but at Exeter Holy Trinity on 21 March 1824 was baptised a William Blanchford, son of William and Susanna Blanchford. The spelling of the surname renders this suggestion questionable, but the two names may have sounded very similar to the parish clerk, especially when spoken with a thick Devonshire accent, and the date fits his majority in June 1844.

William senior was by trade a cabinet maker, albeit not necessarily an overly prosperous one, as he does not feature in the 1850 trade directory. Equally he failed to achieve City Freeman status, which explains why he worked

outside of the city walls. Between 1821 and 1831 his address is recorded as Magdalene Street, a suburban road leading east from the city walls towards Honiton. Between 1819 and 1831 William and Susanna had at least eight children baptised at Holy Trinity, virtually their neighbourhood church, nicely placed for them by the east wall of the city, close to the junction of Magdalene Street and Holloway Street. The church still stands, although now in a rather dilapidated state and used by the White Ensign Club.

We re-enter the realms of the bizarre when it comes to names, for Susanna came from Ugler stock, her marriage to William being recorded at St Leonard's church on 26 December 1818, both signing their names. 'Our' William was their second son. There was a William Henry baptised in 1823, but in all likelihood he died in infancy if there was to be a repetition of the name the following year. St Leonard's church is situated further down Holloway Street, on the road to Topsham. If this lineage is correct, William senior was in his turn the son of William and Sarah Blatchford, and was baptised at Exeter St Paul, in 1795. The hunt goes on for the pre-1795 marriage of William and Sarah, but among a plethora of William Blatchford/ Blanchford/Blanchard and Blachfords in the Mormon IGI Index for Devon between 1750 and 1780, there are just the two outstanding candidates. Of the two William Blatchfords baptised at Exeter St Mary Major in 1769 and 1775, one died early and it would seem that the William baptised in 1775, son of yet another William, is our quarry. William and Elizabeth Smale married by licence in the same church on 5 May 1769, when William was described as 'of Exeter St Sidwell'. This is another large parish church located north of the city wall, and the link is consistent with a family that did not belong to the Freeman class and consequently needed to find work beyond the city limits. Five children were born between 1769 and 1780, four boys and a girl. Only William survived into manhood.

Endurance under stress is clearly a Blatchford characteristic. Trains to Paddington and Waterloo were quick, and Peel's 1844 Act enforcing the operation of a regular third-class service made them cheap, but when five minutes' walk from any point brought one to a slum, the bewildering pattern of London life must have shaken William and Tryphena to the core. Within minutes they became merely a statistic, swallowed by a great and growing city.

Bermondsey happened to be just one of numerous metropolitan areas to feel the impact of increasing numbers of poor people flooding in: Irish navvies for the docks and the railway viaduct, and country immigrants to support and sustain such local industries as leather, jams, metal tins, breweries and all sorts of processed foods. A decade after the Blatchfords made Bermondsey their home, where they remained for over half a century, the scene around them was one of shoddy housing, overcrowding, epidemics, a short expectation of life and incessant work. They may well have reflected that the only difference from Zeal Monachorum could well be summed up in the famous quotation that the same sun which would never set upon the Empire rarely shone on the streets in which they found themselves. Few would claim that Bermondsey in 1848–9 was a blessed area, but it had a distinctive flavour all of its own. The strong scent of brewing was just one of the well-known local odours. Close to Tower Bridge, John Courage's Anchor Brewery made its presence felt, competing with the smell of rotting bones from the soap factories in Carlisle Street and the unforgettable reek from Sarson's Vinegar factory. But of all the unpleasant, smoky and dangerous trades, most pungent of all was the mellow, ripe aroma given off by the substances used in the manufacture of leather.

Before the advent of plastics they used to say 'There's nothing like leather', and ever since the Middle Ages, Bermondsey had been the principal centre in England for the sequence of obnoxious operations and indescribably offensive tasks involved in the tanning business. The River Thames was handily placed – the problem of effluent disposal was one reason why tanneries were located where they were, some of the pre-tanning processes requiring prolonged immersion of the hides in liquid tan-pits, using an amalgam of bird droppings, dog dung or grain fermentation products, all of which were decanted into the river. Immediate access to the docks also allowed for speedy movement of the raw materials imported to

LEFT: *'The Tanner'. A woodcut from a 16th-century German handbook and,* ABOVE: *its equally dangerous 19th-century counterpart.*

remedy the shortage of oak bark, once a feature of the English landscape, even close to hand in Bermondsey as some nearby place names suggest, Forest Hill and Honor Oak. Into this maelstrom plunged the young Blatchfords, pioneers of what became known as the 'Bermondsey spirit'; a jaunty, rugged, two-fingers-to-the-rest-of-the-world fellow feeling. Doubtless they hoped, too, to find a home situated upwind of at least one of forty tanneries in an area of two square miles.

Tanning clung to its slow, laborious and hand-crafted character long after William's arrival. It was a deeply conservative trade, reluctant to accept mechanical aids such as the 'tanning drum', yet it accepted with alacrity one device possibly pertinent to this book, the splitting machine, a most lethal looking contraption, requiring manipulative skill in its operation. In remarkably quick time, the tanner's two-handled knives and the currier's shaving knife for hand paring leathers to the desired thickness were abandoned in favour of a complicated arrangement of band-knives and automated spiral bladed cylinder knives.

The nature of working-class history is such that no trace is to be found of the whereabouts of William and Tryphena for the first couple of years, in what to country folk must have been a hell-hole existence. But we do find that both their older sons, William and Walter, were born in Albert Street, Bermondsey, in the parish of St Mary Magdalene, the latter on 4 February 1851, and on his birth certificate the father's occupation is given simply as 'tanner'. Albert Street has long vanished, wiped out before publication of the large-scale ordnance atlas of 1888, which suggests that it was one of row upon row of tiny back streets and alleys, hastily thrown up to cater for the influx of new workers, lacking proper sanitation and often with only a stand pipe in the street to serve as a water supply. Tanning has always needed skilled craftsmen, but it is idle to pretend that any work involving a sludge of lime and sulphite chromium salts, stale beer, urine and dubbin (tallow and other fatty substances) could have been anything less than brutalising, and it would have given any children lucky enough to have received any sort of education an almost desperate yearning to escape – all the more so if you grew into adulthood right outside one of the larger tanning yards, precisely where Charles Albert was born.

The most important building was the parish church, which in 1830 looked identical to its modern layout. Over one hundred thousand babies have been christened at the church since records were first kept in 1548, and among them are William, Walter, Samuel, and George. All the younger Blatchfords were born at 10 Park Street in Bermondsey, and at the time of the 1861 Census all were in residence there, the four oldest children described as 'scholars' and John, a tiny baby, not yet a year old. Elizabeth was born on 9 December 1856, by which time her father, then aged 32, had graduated to 'journeyman tanner', a skilled artisan in the employ of others, advancing still further to the status of 'leather dresser' by the time the Census took place. He would have been responsible for the conversion of rough leather into a finished, uniform and attractive material, possibly working on a contract basis with outside suppliers. Given the absence of any business records, it makes sense to assume that he was employed by the factory almost on his doorstep, and that at least one of his sons emulated him. Of Devon-born Mary Eliza there is no mention, and she either pre-deceased the 1861 Census or had moved away from the family home.

For the whole family, the sight of their lives would have been the Great Tooley Street Fire at Hay's Wharf in June 1861. It raged for two weeks just down the road from their home, and caused damage estimated at over two million pounds, as well as the death of the Superintendent of the London Fire Engine Establishment when a warehouse exploded. The

St Mary Magdalene Church, Bermondsey. The parish records list several of the Blatchford children.

setting up of the London Fire Brigade as we know it today was a direct result of this spectacular calamity.

Of the oldest son, William, nothing is known and he remains, like the bulk of ordinary Londoners, one of thousands of people who worked hard all their lives, were exploited shamelessly, and only undertook major journeys when it was an urgent or economic necessity. Like all their friends, the Blatchfords would have been street-wise kids, compact, resourceful, self-sufficient and hard. Family legend has it that at least two of the boys were a 'bad lot' and fell foul of the law, but for Charles Albert this grounding gave him a steely, competitive edge and a will to survive when many business rivals went to the wall.

The second son, Walter, maintained the Devon connection in that on Boxing Day 1871 he married Ann Gale, an Okehampton farmer's daughter. At the time of his wedding his address is given as 1 West Road, Spa Street, Bermondsey, a slightly classier neighbourhood

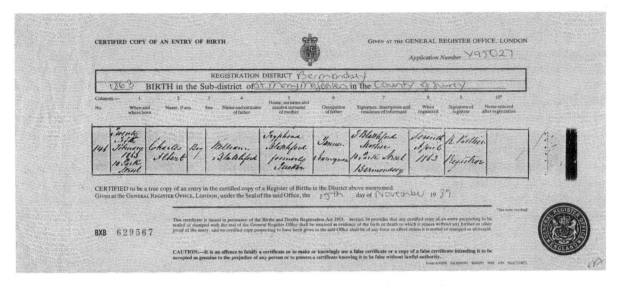

Chas. A. Blatchford's birth certificate.

by local standards, but still only a few hundred yards from Park Street. He died early in 1885, within a few months of the birth of his youngest child, Frank William. His occupation was given as 'wharf manager' and it has been claimed that he was manager of the Hay's Wharf Company, which ran vast tracts of dockland along the south side of the Thames. He is further reputed to have owned his own house in Bousfield Road, quite an achievement in those days for someone in his early thirties. Another family legend, that the earlier Blatchfords at least had a domineering or quarrelsome streak and kept falling out with each other, is given tenuous substance by the fact that his widow was forced to take in dressmaking to keep the family together until the children were old enough to leave home.

Charles Albert Blatchford, the *fons et origo* of this narrative, was born at Park Street on 25 February 1863, the tenth child and youngest son of William and Tryphena, and destined to become their most enduring monument. The Education Act of 1870 made universal education open to all, and whether or not he welcomed the legislation and the resulting foundation of 'Board Schools' dotted piecemeal around Bermondsey, he crept probably unwillingly to school at Bermondsey School for Boys at the junction of Albert and Riley Streets, within 50 metres of his home. As a leathermaker by trade, he followed in his father's footsteps, but what inspired him and his successors to make of a small 'garden-shed' enterprise the thriving company that today bears his name remains conjecture. There were stimuli enough around him. At a time when life was cheap, labour abundant and management not inclined to benevolence, there were in his immediate locality numerous food-processing and packaging firms such as Crosse & Blackwell, Hartley's Jams and Jacob's Biscuits, all using complex equipment which today would be regarded as dangerous. Work on the docks also exposed men to injury, and reference has already been made to the whistling blades of leather technology in the late 1880s. We shall never know whether a single incident, such as an accident to someone close to him which

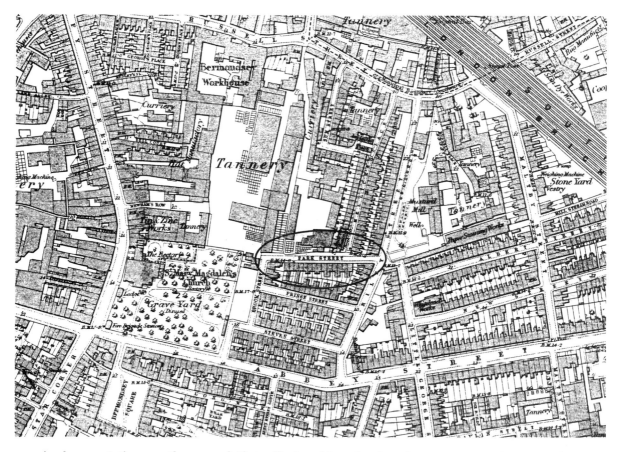

Map showing the environs of the family home in Bermondsey. Park Street, where Chas. was born, is in the centre of the street guide, and an earlier family home in Albert Street, just to the east. Tanneries abound!

required amputation, or the cumulative effects of witnessing years of social neglect within the framework of what the French call *bricolage* – improvisation, filling in gaps, of patching up and making do – prompted Charles to find an outlet for his energies close in spirit to the local people and humanitarian in outlook.

Of course it may have been none of these. Growing up poor in London was no joke, and the looming expanse of wretchedness known as the Bermondsey Workhouse, only a hundred yards to the north-west of his boyhood home, would have been a constant reminder of this. In the other direction, to the north-east, he would have roamed around what is now a highly desirable area of yuppie dockland development,

but in the 1870s and earlier, 'Jacob's Island' as it was called, was quite the most appalling part of the parish. Here, in *Oliver Twist*, Bill Sykes the burglar met his end, amidst tumbledown hovels and sewage filth. As late as the 1950s Bermondsey was known to many locals as 'Stinkpot Alley', and this was after the *Luftwaffe* had dealt it a few resounding blows, so what it was like before the local council took a grip on municipal affairs we can only imagine, and

A mayoral visit to Clapham Road in the late 1920s or early 1930s under the authoritative guidance of Tom Blatchford.

wince. Looking at photographs of Charles one senses about him a sort of Wellsian 'Kipps' air: combative, entrepreneurial, full of bounce yet tough-minded, an ebullient, maverick sort of a chap. President Reagan's farewell words, 'We have earned our optimism, we have a right to our confidence and we have much to do', would for Charles have been more of a curtain-raiser speech.

His handwriting is bold and assertive, his eyes slightly protuberant but cold, the upswept curl of ginger hair almost cocky. Not a large man, he still gives the impression that he could look after himself, with powerful hands and the squashed nose that looks as if it may have had its shape altered down Bermondsey way. He was associated with Charles Bradlaugh of the Rationalist Movement of the late nineteenth century, a modified form of socialism in which, oddly enough, socialism provided a proper foundation for full-blooded individualism. Self-help and the socialist doctrine were seen as complementary, providing there was legislation in force for general social improvement as well, so that it was not left to individuals alone to raise themselves through industry, perseverance and high principles. He has been described as an 'old Edwardian tyrant' in his later years, reluctant to let younger men get ahead or have their own way, but we shall see whether or not this was true.

He is also said to have been something of an innovator, though not necessarily scientific in his approach. One of his inventions was a remarkable glue, but since he had failed to keep any records, he was unable to reproduce it. Before going it alone, he worked with the artificial-limb manufacturers Moses Masters and Sons, who operated from 240 New Kent Road, with works in Paragon Mews, centrally situated between Bermondsey, Newington and Walworth. Long established and prize medallists, of the 16 or so firms in the trade at that time, they were the most geographically accessible.

He probably met his bride-to-be, Mary Campbell, in the Kennington/Camberwell area around 1884, and their marriage followed a couple of years later. Of Scottish origin, she was named after her mother, Mary Parrett, who died as late as 1923, only 14 years before her daughter. Her father, Duncan James Campbell, was a saddler – another link in the leather connection. She is remembered as a 'dear soul', but, more important, she brought in her train two of her three brothers, William and Arthur, who were to prove invaluable to the firm of Blatchfords. Born in Walworth in 1874, this William began in shipping, but worked for the company for the greater part of his life, keeping it going in the years when Chas. was otherwise engaged, before his sons were in a position to take control. Arthur Campbell, the youngest of the three brothers, went to Belfast to set up a branch of Blatchfords, which he ran until his death.

William Blatchford died in May 1890 at the same address in Flinton Street from which Chas. sallied forth on 26 April 1886 to marry Mary.

Nearby, in number 62 Penton Place, Newington, south-east London, he found a site that could not have been more promising. It was to a brand new terraced house, seen at the time as a triumph of working-class architecture, that Charles and Mary took their first born son, Charles Duncan William, forever known as 'Tom' (probably to differentiate him from all the other Blatchfords of similar Christian names). Conveniently close at hand, too, was a recently opened underground station. The street had been one of the first to be laid out and developed on a 99-year lease in the late eighteenth century. These original houses were, with a number of other sites, included in a new building agreement and lease on 2 May 1890, between the Ecclesiastical Commissioners and a property speculator and builder, James Norris, and by July 1891, no. 62 had been built. The Elephant and Castle station, which then served the London, Chatham and Dover Railway, was within a few hundred yards to the north, and some of the arches which carried the railway lines over Manor Place could be clearly seen at the bottom of Penton Place. In November 1890 the underground (City and South London Railway) reached the Elephant and Castle. The first electric railway in the world, it ran from the City, under the Thames and in deep tunnels under Southwark, through the Elephant and on to Kennington, where the original station still stands in Kennington Park Road. The fare was cheap, 2d. all the way. Penton Place was convenient for that major thoroughfare, Kennington Park Road, and was also easily reached by double-decker, horse-drawn trams along the Walworth Road, before their replacement by electric trams using the same lines and just as cheaply priced. Altogether, from the point of view of prospective customers, an eminently satisfactory location.

Charles had been born and raised in a back street somewhat similar to Penton Place, but the terraced houses opposite him were larger and less grim. One step outside and he could survey a dark street where now and then a shadow would pass in front of a curtain, for although many people were engaged in small factories or workshops tucked away in the backyards of homes, the trade directory suggests that this was basically a street of dwelling places. Charles is the only true manufacturer listed – others in the same block included an oilman and a pianoforte tuner. Although he would have been too busy to know, just another few hundred yards away was the infant Charlie Chaplin, born two years before in a room over his grandfather's boot-repair shop in East Street. A choice irony for Charles was the confrontation with two set pieces from his past: leading off Penton Place was yet another Albert Street, and one wonders also whether he suffered tremors of misgivings at the domination of the skyline by the disturbingly close Lambeth Workhouse. After his departure it became the Lambeth Hospital, and was completely destroyed as part of the NHS 'rationalisation'.

CHAPTER TWO

Family History

The firm of Chas. A. Blatchford has always taken 1890 as its starting date, and there is nothing to disprove that Charles was working solo in a small way at that time, but not until 1892 does his name appear in the *Post Office London Directory*, registered at Penton Place as an artificial limb maker. Competition was tough and there were never less than 13 and often as many as 19 firms dabbling in the manufacture of surgical appliances and artificial limbs, all struggling for a portion of what constituted a small business generally. That it was hard going is evidenced by his absence from the classified section of the trade directory again in 1893 and 1894, when Arnold & Sons were 'by Appt. to Bart's'; J. & E. Ferris of Great Russell Street were the 'only makers of legs with sub-astragalus ankle movement' and winners of 17 gold and silver medals; William Robert Grossmith boasted a foundation date of 1760 and medals dating back to 1855, while Philip Gray of Regent Street was the sole manufacturer of the 'Anglesey' artificial leg. It is most likely that the first assignments handled by Charles would have been work subcontracted from Moses Masters or other senior manufacturers, not necessarily selling directly, but subdividing production processes into simple component parts. He emerges as a typical example of the Victorian enterprise culture, one of thousands of small masters who took advantage of a large metropolitan market and pool of useful labour to pioneer their own revolution in production, using very little capital but a lot of ingenuity and human toil, for the operation of inexpensive hand-driven machinery. By 1895 he was able to describe himself with some conviction as an 'Artificial leg, arm, hose and crutch manufacturer to the trade', with a satellite operation at 192 Walworth Road nearby.

Tono Bungay, written by H. G. Wells in 1909, sums up Camberwell as 'endless streets of undistinguished houses, undistinguished industries, shabby families, second-rate shops...' Earlier in the century, the Walworth Road and other main routes to the south were lined with fine town houses for prosperous business and professional people, the roads crowded with signs of Victorian thrust and vigour. But it had become a surface prosperity, the main roads were no longer affluent, now just shopping streets for a suburb changing in both appearance and human content. Always a busy, congested and highly commercialised thoroughfare, the Walworth Road runs south into the Camberwell Road, and was crowded and unlovely, each house exactly like its neighbours.

The building which served as the branch office is now a Bejam shop, still ugly and grimy.

Allowing for interior modernisation, the layout of 62 Penton Place is as it was when Charles left it in 1896. It is three storeys in height, with a narrow entrance hall and steep staircases, and a surprising array of bedrooms. This suggests that both his sons had rooms of their own, or that a 'tweeny' maid was kept, but most likely there would have been lodgers, whose remittances would have been welcome additions to the company purse. The front parlour probably acted as reception and fitting room. A passage leads directly through to what can only have been the assembly area, a large room at the back of the house at ground-floor level, the only room with running water, even at the beginning of this century. This gives access to a miniscule backyard, just large enough for three or so workmen to sprawl at leisure, smoking a pipe during their break.

More spacious accommodation in the neighbourhood was obviously a priority, 126 Camberwell Road seemed to offer it. The elegant and uncluttered façades which once characterised the Camberwell Road had deteriorated with the paraphernalia of generations of private businesses, the long front gardens refaced with shop-fronts, split into flats, laundries, workshops and offices of all kinds. Anyone in Camberwell was within walking distance of one of several railway stations, and an added inducement was the rateable values which in Camberwell were among the lowest in south London. In the 1890s, some 27 per cent of the property in the parish was rated at £20 per annum or less, indicative of an unusually large proportion of small businesses even for an inner London suburb with such a small rate.

Less than a mile to the south-east of Penton Place, but always one crucial step further away from Bermondsey, the new 'factory' was one of over 30 houses between Avenue Road and Wyndham Road. In some streets social demarcation could not be drawn with any precision, for any collection of houses chosen at random could contain all kinds of working-class families, complete with lodgers, as well as small employers who kept a servant or two. Next door to the new premises was Lewis Levy's lodging house and a certain Ernest Rota, newsagent, whose daughter, Susan, later became a Blatchford. Then came serried ranks of self-employed people: Miss Florence Shaw, a specialist in mantle-making, the French Cigarette Company, a watchmaker, coach builders, a collar dresser, coffin maker and a coterie of print shops.

Towards the end of 1903, Rota took over no. 126 and Blatchford moved operations to 43 Parkhouse Street in Camberwell. Contemporary maps make no sense of this move, so short in distance diagonally east, but it was here that Tom grew to manhood and joined the company in a working capacity. In the 1840s Parkhouse Street had luxuriated in the rural atmosphere of stuccoed ornamental cottages and small villas, and although its proximity to the Camberwell Road had ruined any pretensions to countryside, early in the twentieth century its curious curved shape and tree-lined pavements still have lingering village overtones. Where once Blatchfords operated, on a north side corner site next door to Mrs Elizabeth Gaye's laundry, there is now a wholly anonymous factory building.

By 1906 the Ferris company had won two more medals, Masters talked of an illustrated catalogue available upon application, there were 19 rival firms and Blatchfords had made the momentous move to 90 Clapham Road in Lambeth, SW9. In the trade directory, the advertisement described the firm as a 'maker of surgical appliances', followed the next year by reference to the 'highest award given in this country for artificial limbs', and a note on wholesale, retail and *export* business. No. 88 on

Chas. in a South London garden, c. 1913.

grounds, aspired to join a smarter set. Thus it was that while settled in the solid surroundings of Clapham Road he met and was fascinated by 'Florrie' Lambert. A soubrette who had been on the stage with Marie Lloyd, and who could claim among her admirers Stan Laurel, she would have been in her mid-twenties when the romance began. Her father, William Lambert, was a ship owner on a small scale, with links to a bank of the same name in Brussels. Florrie was well connected on the fringes of the Lily Langtry set, she was good looking and an obvious attraction for any married man. Chas. may have refused to marry her, but it was a solid long-term relationship and the indications are that he may have left his wife and family to live with her for a spell, or at least spent a lot of time in her company and settled upon her in his lifetime a discretionary income. She gave birth to a son on 3 November 1911, and he took as his name Charles William Lambert Blatchford. On his marriage certificate dated January 1939, his mother appears as Mrs. Florence E. Pierpoint, principal witness to the ceremony, but clear confirmation of his paternity is given by the way the late Chas. A. Blatchford managed to have the last word. Quixotically, an extra forename has been added and he has become Charles William Albert Blatchford!

To what extent Mary Blatchford and her sons were conscious of this shadow life we cannot know. Suffice it to say that an awareness of some of the more uproarious social gatherings made the younger son, William Arthur David (named for his Campbell uncles and forever known as 'W.A.'), then at a vulnerable and impressionable age, an abstemious man all his life. His older brother, Tom, was born on 23 November 1886 and had by 1914 joined the firm. Early in 1920 he became a director and joint major shareholder, with the same number of shares, 4,500, as W.A. From his father he inherited a buoyant personality, easy going and full of fun

the adjoining corner, always appears to have been a lodging house or private hotel, while running alongside the relatively palatial new premises was a mixture of mortgage brokers, a stained-glass manufacturer, shop fitters, the 'sole maker of "Daniels" patents' and a useful selection of doctors' surgeries.

Always a bon vivant, ripe for the distractions life can offer, Charles was by now in his early forties. He was reasonably well off, and, like many self-made men from humble back-

Tom marries Susan Rota, 31 July 1913. Taken in the back garden of the Rota shop, Chas. and Mary are seated extreme right. W. A. is a boyish figure in the back row.

and, despite an age difference of eight years, the two brothers got on well. The overall impression is that by this time Chas. had shelved most office preoccupations, retaining only crucial decision-making as his particular preserve and leaving routine office management to his sons. As a forcing ground for potential corporate and personal friction, few things could have bettered a situation such as this.

On 31 July 1913 at the parish church, Camberwell, Tom married a boyhood sweetheart, Susan Margherita Rota. He was 26 and his bride four years younger. The witnesses included a name already mentioned in this story – Ernest (Ernesto) Rota, a newsagent, now based at 12 Peckham Road. On the marriage certificate Tom's address is given as 1 Benhill Road and his occupation as 'manufacturer', the same as his father, who dominates the wedding group photograph but did not sign the register, leaving that to W.A., who was presumably acting as best man. The leather link which began with the Campbell family carried on, in that Rota had married Susan Atcheler, whose parents, George and Sarah, made leather trunks and cases, Sarah hand-lining them with quilted satin. Tom passed away in 1938, a victim of the immense strain imposed upon all concerned by the loss of the Ministry of Pensions contract in 1935. Their children, Joan Mary and Kenneth Rota Blatchford, play no part in this family chronicle, although it should be noted that Joan's second husband is the distinguished medical scientist Professor Sir Richard Doll and that Joan herself has been a qualified medical practitioner for many years.

During the First World War, despite many protestations on his part, W.A. was deemed to be in a reserved occupation and therefore

W. A. heads the Cardiff Office staff. A photograph taken in the early 1920s.

ineligible for call-up. At the age of 21 he took over the running of the Cardiff branch, then an important part of the company. The experience thus gained proved invaluable, for as Managing Director he alone saved the firm from near extinction when the contract referred to above was lost in 1935. He had always been an ardent motorist and between 1924 and 1926, when the company was in full flood with the government contract, he managed to cover some 75,000 miles of hard driving. Now, left virtually alone to make what he could of a terrible situation, W.A. was consumed with hard work, worry and the many journeys to be made in his Talbot motor car. Superimposed upon this were the demands made upon an

essentially private, albeit warm-hearted person by the social side of business. Just 41, with three children, he suddenly found the firm without 90 per cent of its business and the enormous pressure brought on ulcers. Despite this, from 1933 to 1955 he was the mainstay of the company, his innate self-belief and endurance showing him to be a carbon copy of his father.

Born on 6 March 1894, at Penton Place in the subdistrict of St Mary Newington, W.A. married Daisy Capewell on 17 July 1917. She was a local girl, part of a large harmonious family, and they had initially met by chance at dancing classes. Their daughter, Joyce, remembers her as a shy, reserved person, very particular in her ways, intelligent, but because of educational limitations never an intellectual. With her husband she created in their four-bedroomed, detached house in Streatham, a cosy, sheltered life for the children.

Very much a man of his time and social class, in an era when people did not slip immediately into first-name terms, and corporate entertainment was limited to a bottle or two at Christmas, W. A. lived for his business and his family. As his son-in-law, Alan Matthews, recalls, he made a point of being at work by 8.30 every morning, also on several Saturdays, and not leaving his office until most of the workforce had gone home. Arts and literature were only of marginal interest, though he would occasionally look in at a Dulwich Hamlet football match and he was a regular attender at Rotary Club meetings. Of a calm, tolerant and retiring

Sharing W. A.'s motoring enthusiasm are his wife, Daisy, with Joyce and Brian, c.1934.

disposition, with the nervous mannerism of picking at his trouser seams, he was never a public person nor possessed of an especially strong personality. On the other hand, no one doubted the strength of his character. He was master both of his job and of his business, and as a technical innovator his flair for engineering was given full rein, so that the company's technical lead became respected throughout the country. Daisy died in 1966, W.A. in 1971, and to his second son, Brian Geoffrey, he bequeathed his strong creative instinct.

Brian was clearly his father's son, both in temperament and motivation. He joined the firm and was both an extremely able engineer as well as being very practical in his approach. He was motivated by his great desire to improve the quality of the artificial limbs provided for amputees, and the running of the business

The marriage of W. A. to Daisy Capewell, July 1917. Chas. and Mary seated extreme left, Tom top left.

followed this aim. Brian shared W.A.'s inventive flair, but as an engineer his approach was more systematic, channelled and tempered. While still at school, for instance, he designed an elbow joint and did drawings at Roehampton with Hugh Steeper. Like his father, slimly built and quiet and reticent in manner, he was a kind and considerate person, with a gentle and compassionate approach to patients which is vividly recalled by many. Freddie James, an independent prosthetist and a veteran in the trade,

remarked that 'Everybody loved Brian without exception. He was *the* most likeable man in the industry, never a word said against him. He was a bit *special*.' In many ways an 'inward-looking person', he is remembered as someone who, although not pushy, was no pushover. Firm in his resolve, sometimes stubborn and conservative while making up his mind, lips pursed with determination, Brian knew where he was going and could clamp down when it mattered.

Born on 12 September 1926, his earliest education included a preparatory boarding school in Eastbourne, where he was sent to improve his health and 'bring him out of himself'. From there he went to St Edward's,

Bill Blatchford, with his wife Valda, left; and Lady Malmesbury.

Brian and Joyce, with the Earl of Malmesbury, Lord Lieutenant of Hampshire.

Oxford, before reading for a B.Sc. in engineering at Battersea Polytechnic. In 1956 he met May Joyce Faulkner, from Midhurst in Sussex, at a Streatham Young Conservatives function in the part of south London where W.A. was then living, and they were married at St Leonard's church, Streatham, on 5 October 1957. In his choice of a partner for life, Brian was fortunate. An old advertising aphorism claims that the hand that rocks the cradle holds the purse strings, and while Brian was very much his own man, Joyce was there to act as a sounding board for his ideas, ever conscious herself of the integrity of the firm. A woman of sound common sense, a director for over 20 years and now a major shareholder, she would represent Blatchfords with her husband at outside functions such as exhibitions and dinners for overseas customers. Both of them, however, preferred to offer hospitality at home, a course of action endorsed with pleasure by many

guests, including, she instances, David Mitchell MP. Outside of business, Brian's chief passion was photography, and his widow recalls him winning the South London Cup, with pictures on display outside the local Astoria Cinema, in Streatham. He also did a lot of his own developing of colour transparencies when they were still relatively uncommon and had to be chilled in the kitchen refrigerator.

The eight year age difference, meant that there was never a great deal of mixing between Brian and his older brother, William Charles (Bill), but with maturity they grew much closer. This attachment became especially close on the business and technical side, since Bill has been for many years the non-executive Chairman of the company. Also, as a Chartered Patent Agent with Withers and Rogers (formerly J. S. Withers and Spooner) for over 40 years, Bill's expertise piloted many Blatchford patents through their various stages. Bill was born in Cardiff on 9 June

An informal meeting of the company's shareholders: Joyce Blatchford (seated, right) with Monica Cooper (née Blatchford), Michael Blatchford and Stephen Blatchford (Managing Director).

1918. His background was that of a sheltered home and good schools, and he learned about life on the lower deck of a warship during the Second World War, finally emerging with the rank of Lieutenant(S), R.N.V.R. He married Valda Reeves in 1950, and any history of this company is indebted to the wealth of genealogical detail accumulated by their son, William Michael. William Michael's sister, Monica

Frances (Cooper), and he were born in Croydon, and both are now joint minority shareholders in the company, with William Michael inheriting his father's mantle as the Blatchford Patent Agent and also entitled to add the qualification CPA to his name.

Sandwiched between the Blatchford brothers is W.A.'s only daughter, Joyce Lilian, born on 12 October 1920, and mother of Jill Elizabeth (Nunn) and Robert Edwin Matthews. An engaging and vivacious lady, her abiding memories of 90 Clapham Road are the sense of awe she felt in the presence of Chas. and Mary, the dark and dismal appearance of the place, made overpoweringly noisy by the din of belt-driven machinery. She met Alan Matthews on a farmhouse holiday in Devon when she was 14 and he was playing in a rugby match at the local school. She was watching over the hedge, gave him some of her packet of sweets, never tried to wean him from his love of rugby, and married him ten years later. Alan went into the Royal Air Force straight out of school and trained at Cranwell. A radar specialist (IFF and ASV), and blessed with an inventive mind, it was recommended after discharge from active service that he should go into the firm to learn the trade. This he did, from the bottom upwards, retiring in 1985 as Office Manager after almost 40 years of service.

Brian was supremely knowledgeable about matters relating to the firm's design work, and ever-receptive to fresh ideas, but as a manager he largely allowed others to run the day-to-day work of the company. Responsible for the creation of a Research Unit at the factory in Basingstoke, with the necessary Drawing Office and talented engineers to implement his sophisticated skills, he would nevertheless be the first to admit that the company needed a 'front man'. Forthright and outspoken, 'Tommy' Thompson, Director of Prosthetics, fitted the bill perfectly, and much credit should go to him for making the company successful and international. It was doubly unfortunate that the period of Thompson's retirement coincided with the sudden death of Brian on Christmas Eve 1985, for it propelled his son, Stephen, somewhat abruptly into a position where as Harry S. Truman put it, 'the buck stops'.

Stephen had already been in the firm from 1 September 1985 as a management trainee working with the Drawing Office staff where his specialist computer training was likely to prove useful, but the planned run-in period and transfer of power over three to five years were inexorably cut to four months with the rapid

Stephen Blatchford, Managing Director since December 1985 and great-grandson of Chas.

deterioration in his father's health. An immediate council of war was held and it was decided that Stephen should take charge straightaway, rather than allow an interim period when matters might drift. More dynamic than his father, adroit in moving with changing times and essentially a pragmatic man prepared to take necessary risks (honed perhaps by his quiet passion for computer war-gaming), he had clear thoughts about what should be done. He had, in fact, prior to this swift turn in events, already written a paper on corporate strategy for the future. Nothing, however, in his or anyone else's calculations, had prepared the Board for a three-pronged, concerted broadside upon the industry from the committee led by Professor Ian McColl, the Monopolies and Mergers Commission, and from the government through the far-reaching overhaul of the National Health Service. It can safely be said that Stephen has had it 'just over three years hard'. It is equally fair to say that thanks to an aggressive marketing policy and a readiness to face unpalatable truths, he has done wonders in coping with tribulations not necessarily of his own choosing.

Born in Croydon on 7 December 1959, and educated at the same school as his father, Stephen married Caroline Mary Greenwood in 1986. He was always aware of the latent pressure upon him to join a family firm, with all its appeal of continuity, something of an anachronism in this modern age. He felt, however, that some outside industry experience was mandatory, and having gained a degree in mathematics at St Catherine's, Oxford, followed by an M.Sc. in computation at the Programming Research Group, Oxford, he went on to join ICL at Bracknell as a software program designer. The valuable but frustrating nature of his involvement with ICL's preoccupation with standard giant industrial projections shaped Stephen's belief in small-scale project and design teamwork within the framework of the smaller company. In a sense the wheel has come full circle, for with the departure of the post-1945 sheltered workshop trading climate, and the market-place again a happy hunting ground wide open to all comers, Stephen faces precisely the same challenge to economic survival as confronted his great-grandfather. *Plus ça change ...*

CHAPTER THREE

A History of Artificial Limbs

Prosthesis stems from a Greek word meaning 'addition' (*pros* = to , *thesis* = a placing)

Not all history is bunk, not even paintings of crowd scenes four hundred years old, when the eye is caught by crippled amputees propelling themselves along on platform prostheses which enable them to keep both legs at the same height. The element of grotesque matters less than the suggestion that devices of this nature, the lack of post-operative physiotherapy and subsequent deformity allow us a perspective on modern prostheses and how successful rehabilitation has become.

The history of artificial limbs probably dates from the emergence of intelligent man himself, which makes them as old as humanity. Whatever the motivation for the earliest amputations – ritual sacrifice, cure of disease, magic or punishment – no one knows for certain where and when the first maimed man sought a remedy for his imperfection. Information about early artificial limbs is scarce, but the lower limb, more vital and easier to construct, preceded the upper limb.

Despite war injuries, the cruel punishment of law-breakers, inhuman crippling of war prisoners and endemic disease, all of which must have inspired the production of artificial limbs, ancient Chinese history is silent on the subject. Old Testament scholars, too, have found no conclusive evidence, but there is a note in the Talmud of a cripple supplied with a padded wooden stump and with leather knee pads to protect extremities while shuffling along the ground. Much discussion in the *Mischna* centres on whether or not strict Sabbath law – which forbids the carrying of any objects – also applied to wooden legs.

The earliest mention seems to be in Indian literature, in the *Rig-Veda*, the oldest book of the Veda period, (1500–800 BC), when the use of artificial eyes and artificial teeth, as well as artificial legs, was recorded. This is on a par with the frequently quoted story by Herodotus (485–425 BC) which refers to the wooden foot belonging to the mystical Seer Hegesistratus of Elias, who was imprisoned by the Spartans and held by the immobilisation of one foot in stocks. This he hacked off at the instep, through the

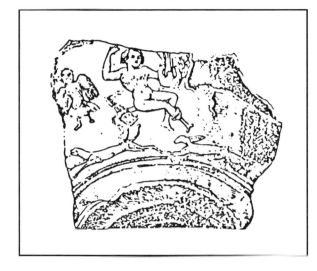

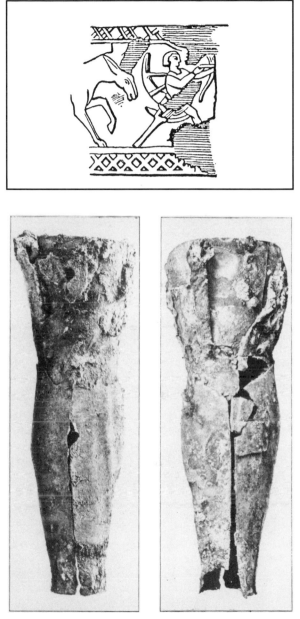

LEFT: *'Beggars and Cripples', attributed to Bruegel, dated c.1550-5. An accumulation of defects far removed from any modern compassionate viewpoint.*

ABOVE: *Pen drawing of a fragment of Ionian vase, showing a figure with a pylon replacing the missing limb.*

ABOVE RIGHT: *Lescar Cathedral mosaic.*

RIGHT: *Roman artificial right leg, dating from the early Christian era, excavated near Capua, and made of bronze plates fashioned to a wooden core.*

Chopart joint, so that he would still be mobile after escape.

Graeco-Roman physicians from Hippocrates to Celsus and Galen describe amputations, but infuriatingly never elaborate upon prosthetic devices. Peg legs were known and used, and the earliest known representation of an artificial limb is on a vase in the Louvre, said to be fourth century BC, depicting a crippled satyr with a peg leg at the knee. A fragment of Ionian pottery found in 1862 shows a naked man sitting in a chair, holding in his left hand a lyre. Two-thirds of the right leg has a peg leg substitute.

Vestigial records of artificial limbs from other ancient civilisations have also been located.

There is an Inca pottery remnant which shows a figure of a man with a leg amputated at the tibiotarsal junction, and holding in his right hand a pointed cap to be adjusted to the stump

'St Martin with his horse in a ship'. In a crowded scene almost akin to bedlam, the eye alights on the solitary figure, bottom right.

of his leg, while the Viking sagas sing of a hero called Trefote, 'wooden foot'. The cathedral in Lescar, in the French Pyrenees, has a mosaic which dates back to the Gallo-Roman era and shows a negro amputee whose leg is supported at the knee by a wooden pylon.

The oldest artificial leg unearthed dates from at least 300 BC and was found in 1858 in a tomb in Capua, Italy. The original, a typical specimen of Roman versatility and ingenious work-manship, was on display at the Royal College of

Surgeons in London until war damage in 1941, but fortunately photographs and descriptions are preserved.

Very little is known about progress in the development of prostheses during the Dark Ages. The limbless were left to fend for themselves. In remoter times, before the use of cannon and half-pound shot on the battlefields of Europe, the necessity of amputation was rare, and the need for artificial limbs correspondingly infrequent. The peg leg, an invention from the earliest times of history, has proved its usefulness as the ideal walking apparatus for the great majority of amputees, especially country people and working men, right through

ABOVE: Man with platform leg support.

RIGHT: Sheet metal plates gave the appearance of armour to disguise the artificial leg as described by Ambroise Paré in 1561.

walking upright with the aid of a bent-knee support and a crutch.

The real breakthrough in surgical technique for amputations was initiated by Ambroise Paré (1509–90). He recommended preferred sites for amputations and designed prostheses with movable joints. He was also the first surgeon to work in close collaboration with artificers, fore-runners of the modern-day prosthetist, of whom a skilled locksmith known as 'le petit Lorrain' was the most famous. In his textbook on surgery published in 1575 he devoted a special chapter to the means of repairing or making good natural or accidental deficiencies in the human body, and his whole approach is marked by an

the centuries up to the present day. The poorest, however, were unable to procure the 'leg of the day' and moved beyond the fringes of society on crutches or movable benches or disks.

An illustration to an otherwise obscure Polish poem published in Cracow in 1612 shows the epic figure of the god Vulcan with a below-knee device, and mute evidence of the frequency with which bent-knee prostheses occur is discernible in various medieval works of art. An amputated beggar wearing a crafted platform support attached to his bandaged leg appears in a fifteenth-century painting by the Master of the Uttenheim Altarpiece. In the 'St Martin ship tableau' from the school of Hieronymus Bosch, painted in the sixteenth century, a man is shown unusual compassion for the problems of handicap. Many of his drawings and descriptions so closely approach those of today that he is rightly called the founder of 'modern principles of amputations'.

In the early part of the seventeenth century, Peter Low in his *Discourses of the Whole Art of Chirugery,* gave representations of artificial legs, but there appears to have been no great demand for above-knee artificial limbs since amputations of that sort were rarely performed. The Zucchini limb, produced in 1616 for the Marquis Francis Riarrio, is another surgical landmark in that the craftsman after whom it was named envisaged a definitive functional or aesthetic object, or both. Vanity or the code of chivalry compelled soldier knights of those days to conceal their mutilations, regarded more as marks of inferiority than courage, and armour designers catered for the concealment of disability by making a complete body armour with but one purpose – the provision of a workable hand for sword or lance to restore battle performance. In 1696 the Dutch surgeon Verduin constructed a below-knee prosthesis with a wooden foot and a copper socket which, after sundry modifications, served as the pattern for modern devices until the 1960s, when the PTB (patella-tendon bearing prosthesis) did away with the Verduin hinged metal side bars.

The artisan mechanic Gavin Wilson of Edinburgh, at the end of the eighteenth century, was the first after Paré to attempt a solution to above-knee prosthesis. His limb creation was fashioned from hardened leather with a knee joint which could be flexed in sitting and it was designed so that the knee stiffened while walking. He also made the first use of what is now known as an 'ischial seat'.

In 1805, a limb maker named James Potts, of Chelsea, London, put through a patent for an artificial leg articulated at the knee, ankle and toe joints, and went on in 1816 to manufacture a first substitute for the limb lost at Waterloo by Henry William Paget, first Marquess of Anglesey (1768–1854). Known also as the 'Clapper leg' for the noise it made when fully extended, the 'Anglesey' was brought to the United States in 1839 by Dr Palmer, himself an amputee. At the Crystal Palace Exhibition of 1851 it was the only wooden leg to receive honourable mention. The improved Palmer 'American leg' was a novel contrivance of artificial tendons within the limb, simulating muscle action for movable knee and ankle joints, and a toe joint dependent upon a spring action. In the late 1850s they were used by 1,200 people in Britain, and permutations on the original remained in use in Britain and France until the First World War.

The advent of general anaesthesia, also in the 1850s, stimulated the technology upon which modern prosthetic art has capitalised. Indeed, the history of artificial limbs almost parallels that of amputations and the slow evolution of prosthetics took place against the background of the pain. All patients endured agony right up to the middle of the last century. A woodcut from a book of surgery published in 1517 claims to show the earliest pictorial representation of amputation, and for well over a thousand years surgeons had to be devoid of all tenderness and pity, entirely deaf to the shrieks of the suffering victim.

Modern surgeons have a variety of techniques at their disposal for the removal of an arm or leg, but their predecessors had but two options – the circular 'guillotine' operation or 'flap jobs'. The first was performed by slicing the soft tissue to the bone just above the damaged area and finishing the job, which most practitioners could do in two or three minutes. More 'advanced' operators shortened the bone and brought flaps of soft tissue down over the end producing a better looking stump, albeit one very vulnerable to infection and slower to heal. In addition, doctors and apothecaries of

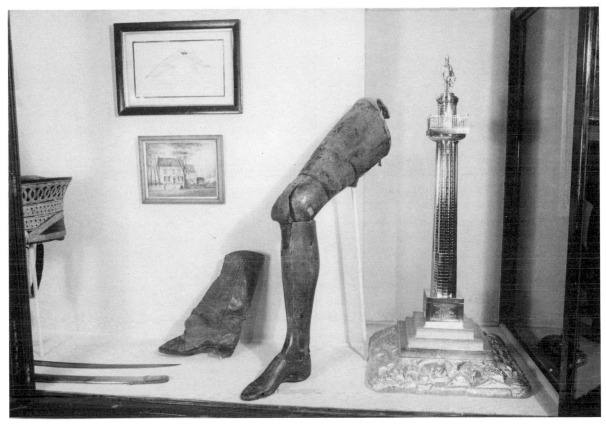

Regalia of the 1st Marquess of Anglesey as General of Hussars, and the famous wooden leg named after him.

the 1850s and 1860s knew scarcely more about pharmacology than did the physicians and priests of ancient times. They were strong on laxatives, leeches and purges, but apart from quinine and morphia were quite happy to try anything that had a medicinal smell or an interesting taste.

War is, of course, the great forcing ground for spectacular innovation, and the Crimean War of 1854–6 fostered the first dim awareness of the futility of tearing the body rather than mending it. Guthrie, Surgeon-General during the war, wrote 'The older I grow, the less I amputate',

and came to believe that arms should be removed only *in extremis* and that wounded soldiers deserved rather more than a 55 per cent mortality rate for both primary and secondary amputations.

The American Civil War just five years later saw carnage on a much greater scale, and doctors were overwhelmed by endless lines of men needing amputation. The rationale that wounded men are a greater liability to one's opponents than the dead was well understood and underscored by the order 'Fire at their feet'. The large numbers of amputation cases gave an impetus to the design and manufacture of prostheses, so that a wide circle of limb makers got their living there. Roughly three out of every four men wounded were hit in the extremities,

Serratura.

Agony and surgery were inseparable in the centuries pre-anaesthesia. Woodcut from a surgical treatise, 1517. A doubled fist close at hand represents anaesthesia.

and the shattering, splintering effect on bone of the Minié musket ball was infinitely worse than the clean hole left by high-impact bullets. Severe shot wounds usually resulted in bone fractures, which commonly led to amputation.

A decent splint to immobilise the parts temporarily until hospitalisation would have been an asset, but surgery of the mid-nineteenth century not only ignored ancient practices but was appreciably worse. The schism between surgeons and physicians had forced surgical practice into the hands of the unskilled, untutored and itinerant. In the Anglo-Saxon world the physician was a reputable man of science, the surgeon a part-time barber. Under the surgical practice of the day, germs of blood poison were conveyed directly into the body. Deadly infections set in rapidly in the wake of the saw and scalpel. Knife-happy surgeons forced potential amputees to vanish into the bush or hide guns under their pillows rather than become another statistic in *The Medical and Surgical History of the War of the Rebellion*.

The fatality rate for amputations of the extremities ranked with that of the Crimea, but one of the fortunate survivors was a Colonel J. E. Hanger, who lost a limb at the Battle of Bull Run. He made for himself an artificial leg to enable him to re-enter the struggle. This proved very successful and he was soon making limbs for fellow soldiers who were similarly afflicted. His son set up the firm of J. E. Hanger & Co. in England after the First World War.

Old soldiers never die, they simply fade away and become politically impotent. This was not necessarily true of the civilian arena. In the United States amputation was a much commoner operation, not because of any lack of conservative surgery, but because the increased tempo of mechanisation had made accidents more common. Gradually the limb maker ceased to be just a specially skilled carpenter or blacksmith and evolved into a trained prosthetist who worked in shops specialising in the manufacture of artificial limbs. While others tried to design ankle and foot joints which imitated the natural motion, the Marks company in America built the rubber foot and Hanger built the cordless ankle, using rubber bumpers for control of movement. Neither type permitted lateral motion but they increased the safety and stability of the wearer. In 1858 Douglas Bly designed a limb with a ball-and-socket ankle mechanism, useful for slopes and uneven surfaces. The suction socket and roller knee, introduced in America by Dubois Parmalee, was intended to reduce friction, and by dispensing with body straps was a great improvement.

Called by a German writer 'the indefatigable inventor of inexpensive and practical artificial limbs for the poor', Count Beaufort designed a limb which was simple to make, inexpensive, and was seen primarily as a working men's leg to replace the old-fashioned peg. Widely used during the First World War, it was highly regarded in medical circles as late as 1929. As a replacement for steel parts, aluminium was introduced into prostheses in the 1860s.

The dichotomy between surgeons who shrugged off any responsibility for the amputees' subsequent rehabilitation and limb makers who were as ignorant of the surgeons' limitations as the surgeons were of theirs was long a source of irritation to the limb makers. On the one hand, no surgeon could design or carry out an amputation successfully if the resulting stump was one to which an artificial limb could not be conveniently attached. Equally, it was useless to devise a limb, however perfect in theory, if it could not be borne by the patient's stump. Yet it was the limb maker alone who had to assume post–operative responsibility and treat the amputee at his discretion. Largely ignored, and rarely invited to point out the best place of election in surgery, their subordinate position in the medical hierarchy is further illustrated by the general situation in Britain.

In St Thomas's Hospital, which could be taken as a microcosm of the country at large, in 1913 – the year immediately before the First World War – out of 5,483 major operations undertaken, there were only 34 amputations; a proportion of 1:161. That year, too, the Royal Surgical Aid Society, responsible for all types of appliances not only in London but also in the provinces, supplied only 529 artificial peg legs

and arms out of 41,483 appliances. In short, as an industry, limb-making of the homespun, indigenous variety was as peripheral as any documentation to be found which bears on the situation in Britain.

In spite of the thickets of self-congratulatory verbiage in Frederick Gray's book *Automatic Mechanism* (1855), the lingering impression is one of monied patients by and large getting a cheapjack parcel, asking for rubbish and paying for it, and scarcely a word against. The earliest of our limb mechanicians were probably without much schooling, without wealth or poverty, travelling without labels in the guard's van of the larger Victorian social express. But which of these discreet men doing a discreet job was first on the scene is difficult to discern. A clue of sorts is offered in *The Lancet* of 1 November 1862, with its extensive coverage of the Great International Exhibition. Then as now, trade exhibitions of surgical instruments were essentially a showplace for firms which represented advances in the production of new commodities, instruments and appliances. With this solitary exception, the animated discussions between medical practitioners and the people ready to supply them with the latest developments never mention artificial limbs. At the Great International Exhibition, however, limbs exhibited by the 'old established houses' of Bigg and Grossmith, 'highly reputed for upwards of a century', were well received. Bigg won praise for the lateral rotative motion of the ankle joint by means of a ball and socket invented and patented by Bly of Rochester, USA, and Grossmith for a novel spring principle which connected the action of the knee and ankle joints. Another firm whose patent work was noticed was that of Moses Masters, 'remarkable for the most exquisite finish'. He displayed the only complete series of artificial limbs which were said truly to exemplify original thought. His knee spring permitted the

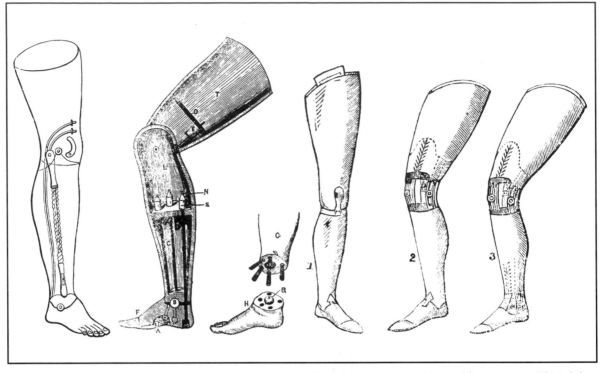

From the Great International Exhibition at St Thomas's Hospital, 1862, a display of new limbs from Bigg and Grossmith. Also shown were knee spring and flexible toe 'improvements' by Mr Masters, identical to those in his 1848 advertisement.

lower leg to recoil to a natural angle, and a flexible toe mechanism dispensed with the wooden joint and steel bolt. It was reckoned, too, that the Masters perforated concave hinge was a blessing for below-knee amputees; it was lighter and stronger than any other hinge, almost frictionless and therefore durable, while the concavity allowed it to lie closer to the leg. It was among this company of experts that Chas. Blatchford was later to learn his craft.

Little is known of the pre-1840s activities of any of the firms mentioned in this book. It was in the 1840s, when Sheldrake, Bigg and Company (afterwards Henry Bigg and Son)

drew attention to its self-acting artificial leg recently invented; by means of 'India-rubber Tendons', the action of the knee and ankle joints were 'rendered as perfect as those of the natural limb'. Vying with Bigg for the honour of being the oldest established British company was the firm founded around 1760 by John Henry Sleath. As Sleath & Williamson, it was transformed by marriage in 1845 into W. R. Grossmith, a very well known name in the trade until comparatively recent times. Sleath appears in *The Universal British Directory* (1793) as a truss maker, operating from a Fleet Street address, but he had obviously been around some time as in that year he was granted a patent for the manufacture of springs for trusses and coverings thereof (*Alphabetical Index of Patentees of Inventions 1617–1852*). John Williamson was one of three artificial limb manufacturers, along with 32 truss makers, listed in Pigot's *London and Provincial New Commercial Directory* (1826–7), with a historically helpful sales pitch:

> 'The only real maker of patent artificial legs and hands of upwards of twenty years practice...[patients] can be supplied with artificial legs, above or below the knee, on the lightest, most durable and best principle; also from one finger to a whole hand and arm complete, with a variety of useful implements. [He offered] knee-joint pin legs, for ease in sitting down, and the securest ever invented, and common pin legs of every description, false calves for wasted or deformed legs...'

William Robert Grossmith picked up medals for his products at the great Crystal Palace Exhibition of 1851, and his patent leg in the 1860s was said to be much lighter and less expensive than the old style of cork leg. It lasted a lifetime and was the only one yet invented that women and children could wear with safety. His honours board became replete with subsequent awards, Moses Masters was also honoured: London 1851, 1862, 1873; Paris 1867, Brussels 1876; Cutler's Hall 1879.

Then there was the marvellously named H. J. Stump (later Stump and Gray), who set up in business in February 1863 after nine years' pupillage at the house of Frederick and Philip Gray. His advertisements make the rather bizarre claim not to have exhibited anywhere. Companies which did exhibit regularly and picked up a drum roll of medals were John Weiss and Sons and Frederick Gustav Ernst, whose wife 'waited upon ladies' in the 1850s, and who described himself a decade later as an 'Orthopaedic, Anatomical and Gymnastic Machinist'. His particular name is perpetuated in Vokes Ernst Scientific Surgical Appliances Ltd (Vessa) of Alton. Many came and went and are now but names: Henry Simpson, Joseph Pratt (by appointment to The Army Medical Board and sole agent for the Beaufort Limb),

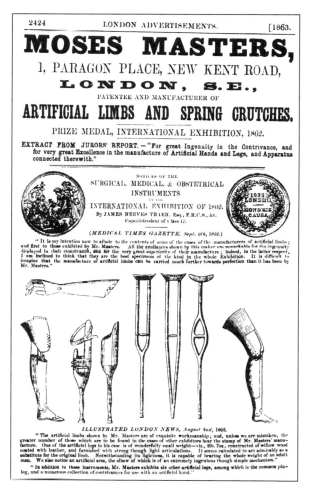

An advertisement for the firm of Moses Masters, where Chas. first learnt his craft.

Charles Salmon, Arnold and Sons, and J. & E. Ferris, medal winners at the Royal Military Exhibition of 1890. Favourable reference was made in the *British Medical Journal* (14 October 1905) to the remedial work of Mr Gillingham of Chard, and his catalogues at least survive in safe keeping at the Science Museum.

The Victorian age was one of ingenuity and investigation, and *The Lancet* critique of 1862 not only hints at an inspiring degree of patient care

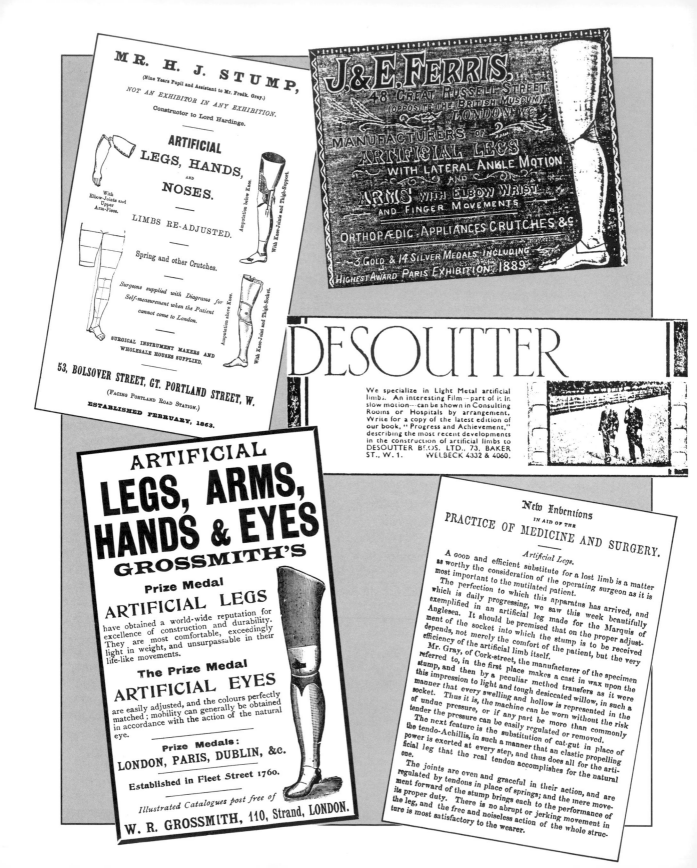

MR. H. J. STUMP,

(Nine Years Pupil and Assistant to Mr. Fredk. Gray.)

NOT AN EXHIBITOR IN ANY EXHIBITION.

Constructor to Lord Hardinge.

ARTIFICIAL
LEGS, HANDS,
AND
NOSES.

With Elbow-Joints and Upper Arm-Piece.

Amputation below Knee.

With Knee-Joint and Thigh-Support.

LIMBS RE-ADJUSTED.

Spring and other Crutches.

Surgeons supplied with Diagrams for Self-measurement when the Patient cannot come to London.

Amputation above Knee.

With Knee-Joint and Thigh-Socket.

SURGICAL INSTRUMENT MAKERS AND WHOLESALE HOUSES SUPPLIED.

53, BOLSOVER STREET, GT. PORTLAND STREET, W.

(FACING PORTLAND ROAD STATION.)

ESTABLISHED FEBRUARY, 1863.

J. & E. FERRIS,
48 GREAT RUSSELL STREET
(OPPOSITE THE BRITISH MUSEUM)
LONDON, W.C.

MANUFACTURERS OF

ARTIFICIAL LEGS
WITH LATERAL ANKLE MOTION
AND
ARMS WITH ELBOW WRIST
AND FINGER MOVEMENTS

ORTHOPÆDIC APPLIANCES CRUTCHES &c.

3 GOLD & 14 SILVER MEDALS INCLUDING
HIGHEST AWARD PARIS EXHIBITION 1889.

DESOUTTER

We specialize in Light Metal artificial limbs. An interesting Film—part of it in slow motion—can be shown in Consulting Rooms or Hospitals by arrangement. Write for a copy of the latest edition of our book, "Progress and Achievement," describing the most recent developments in the construction of artificial limbs to DESOUTTER BROS. LTD., 73, BAKER ST., W.1. WELBECK 4332 & 4060.

ARTIFICIAL
LEGS, ARMS,
HANDS & EYES
GROSSMITH'S

Prize Medal
ARTIFICIAL LEGS

have obtained a world-wide reputation for excellence of construction and durability. They are most comfortable, exceedingly light in weight, and unsurpassable in their life-like movements.

The Prize Medal
ARTIFICIAL EYES

are easily adjusted, and the colours perfectly matched; mobility can generally be obtained in accordance with the action of the natural eye.

Prize Medals:
LONDON, PARIS, DUBLIN, &c.

Established in Fleet Street 1760.

Illustrated Catalogues post free of

W. R. GROSSMITH, 110, Strand, LONDON.

New Inventions
IN AID OF THE
PRACTICE OF MEDICINE AND SURGERY.

Artificial Legs.

A GOOD and efficient substitute for a lost limb is a matter as worthy the consideration of the operating surgeon as it is most important to the mutilated patient.

The perfection to which this apparatus has arrived, and which is daily progressing, we saw this week beautifully exemplified in an artificial leg made for the Marquis of Anglesea. It should be premised that on the proper adjustment of the socket into which the stump is to be received depends, not merely the comfort of the patient, but the very efficiency of the artificial limb itself.

Mr. Gray, of Cork-street, the manufacturer of the specimen referred to, in the first place makes a cast in wax upon the stump, and then by a peculiar method transfers as it were this impression to light and tough desiccated willow, in such a manner that every swelling and hollow is represented in the socket. Thus it is, the machine can be worn without the risk of undue pressure, or if any part be more than commonly tender the pressure can be easily regulated or removed.

The next feature is the substitution of cat-gut in place of the tendo-Achillis, in such a manner that an elastic propelling power is exerted at every step, and thus does all for the artificial leg that the real tendon accomplishes for the natural one.

The joints are even and graceful in their action, and are regulated by tendons in place of springs; and the mere movement forward of the stump brings each to the performance of its proper duty. There is no abrupt or jerking movement in the leg, and the free and noiseless action of the whole structure is most satisfactory to the wearer.

on the part of some prosthetists, but also that the problem of dealing with inclines and downward slopes was already uppermost in their thinking. Set against this is the savage indictment of his contemporaries by Frederick Gray, who in *Automatic Mechanism*, said that their crude and almost inartificial means to supplement the loss of limbs betrayed wholesale incompetence, their feeble efforts producing only instruments of torture. For their part, Grays took the credit for having by 1848 'brought to its present perfection' the original invention by Potts of the Anglesey leg, which, like all originals, had defects and could not cope initially with cases of people either fat or thin and spare. Now 'Hundreds of persons are at this moment by my means in a state of comparative comfort, and enjoying from my substitutes for amputated limbs an alleviation from pain and misery which, till within a very few years, would have been considered…beyond the range of hope'. These amputees before they were placed in his care, were quite out of heart, suffering from excoriation of the stump. Patients who wore Gray's invention were said to walk well, ride to hounds, climb trees, play cricket and be accomplished rough shootists. They were often mentioned in society magazines because of their presence at dances. They came to him as a result of tiger bites, railway, steamboat and carriage accidents, cliff falls, firework explosions and the horrible but inevitable calamities of war. Routine geriatric disablements, the very stuff of our prosthetic service today, are ignored.

Quite apart from its claim to be the first book on the construction of artificial limbs, *Automatic Mechanism* lifts the veil on the social position of patients and the means whereby the limb maker won patronage and drummed up trade. Some

LEFT: *Mr H. J. Stump heads a montage of advertisements for rival firms to Chas. A. Blatchford.*

patients were brought or sent to Gray by about 30 named surgeons, such as Professor Syme of Edinburgh or Sir Benjamin Brodie, others were received by private and personal recommendation. Some female cases are described but his patients were mainly aristocratic sprigs, young gentlemen of fortune, diplomats, clergymen, Members of Parliament, doctors and an assortment of British, Russian and Austrian military personnel. Senior ranking officers included Sir Thomas Trowbridge, who lost both legs at Inkerman in the Crimean War, and Lord Hardinge, Governor-General of India.

For some, benefit societies defrayed all expenses incurred, but while medical progress was enthusiastically welcomed by those who could afford it, the less fortunate relied on active benevolence from the more affluent sectors of society, or upon the casual bounty of the local parson. As much as 28 per cent of people in urban areas seldom could afford hospitalisation or a visit to the doctor's surgery. They depended on the generosity of individual medical men for any lasting attention. This precluded any possibility of availing themselves of the improved artificial limbs of the day – their sole resort was the common peg leg.

Private charity tends to be temporary and exhaustible, but nevertheless by the 1890s, when Chas. A. Blatchford appeared on the scene, most manufacturers had agents in provincial towns, even on the Continent, and illustrated prospectuses with diagrams for self-measurement were available upon application from surgeons, when the patient could not come to London. When the most trifling variation in a leg can be crucial, it seems curious that limb manufacturers would supply their work to patients whom they had never seen, and who were invited by advertisement to send by letter a measurement of their legs without even a wax case of the stump to indicate its exact shape. Nevertheless these trade catalogues were

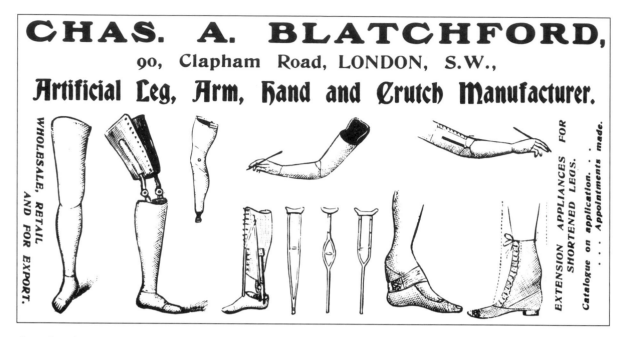

CHAS. A. BLATCHFORD,

90, Clapham Road, LONDON, S.W.,

Artificial Leg, Arm, Hand and Crutch Manufacturer.

WHOLESALE, RETAIL AND FOR EXPORT.

EXTENSION APPLIANCES FOR SHORTENED LEGS. . . Catalogue on application. . . . Appointments made.

An early advertisement from the Edwardian era.

printed in large quantities and in multiple editions.

By 1902, Chas's old employers, Masters and Son, had passed their half-century and were now well endowed as 'Contractors to the Army, Navy and most of the charitable institutions'. A map printed in the *Daily Mail* that year, showing vast tracts south of the River Thames almost bereft of major hospitals, doubtless gave a keener edge to the competition between Masters and Blatchfords. Social conscience dictated that the sick and disabled poor should be able to obtain relief near to where they lived, but the population of this corner of south-east London amounted to only about two hundred thousand, so local clients must have been few, even after 1903 when King's Hospital was shifted to a site in Camberwell.

Publicity became paramount and in 1907, a year after the move to Clapham Road, Chas.

was moved to take the unprecedented step of having a whole-page advertisement in the *London County Suburbs Directory*. Reference is made to the 'highest award given in this country for artificial limbs', but this is, frankly, diffident by comparison with other firms, most of which Chas., as a 'maker of surgical appliances', was to outlast. When speaking of competition and the direction in which money had to be spent, it has to be remembered that the *total* number of artificial limbs made in England before the First World War was probably less than the number supplied in one month from the killing fields, and that even better paid workers still relied heavily on private charities to pay for treatment. As early as 1810 there were seven thousand 'friendly societies' enjoying legal status and protection for the future; some leading railway companies, for instance, had a provident fund; and most employees paid regular weekly contributions into insurance schemes run by trade unions and benefit clubs. A clientele such as this, before the National Insurance Act was approved by Parliament in 1911, helps explain the constant reiteration in trade catalogues of the inexpensive nature and accessibility of medical apparatus.

The oldest extant *Catalogue of Artificial Legs, Arms, Hands, Crutches, and Extension Appliances...manufactured by Charles A. Blatchford* is a revised edition of an earlier publication from 126 Camberwell Road. The 80-page manual is as much a sober and impartial anatomical treatise as an appeal for custom, and it has a period charm all of its own. Dated about 1907, Chas. proclaims the 'self satisfaction of supplying a limb superior to our competitors' and no less than 200 line drawings suggest he was prepared to tackle anything and everything by way of modifications, adjustments and improvements. Few claims are made as yet for originality of design. On offer is a modified Anglesey leg as well as a cheaper, tendonless limb for working men; varieties of below-knee limbs, either with an ordinary finish or enamelled after the American style; and legs adapted for Syme's and Chopart's amputations. Also, 'For charitable institutions, and poor people who cannot afford to go to price of artificial limbs, we make varieties of substitutes with pins'. An honest and conscientious effort was promised with American and Continental patterns, based on Chas's best judgement as to value and practicality. The advantages of having a patent adjustable tendon placed in the leg are stressed and the different classes of limb most commonly in use fairly outlined.

One enamelled limb for a thigh amputation has an ankle joint of note, with back and fore movement in its upper portion, and lateral movement in the lower, and of this Chas. wrote:

'I can say without fear of contradiction it is the *strongest ankle-movement made* in the United Kingdom at the present time. This leg has been under a patent for twelve years, which has now became void

Catalogue of
Artificial Legs,
Arms, Hands, Crutches,
and
Extension Appliances,
&c., &c.,

MANUFACTURED BY

Charles A. Blatchford,

90, Clapham Road,
London, S.W.
(Near Kennington Church).

(Late 126, Camberwell Road.)

Title page of the first known catalogue, probably dated c. 1907.

through non-payment of fees, and this is the first time we have been able to supply the trade with it. I was the first man to make this leg in England under the instruction of the inventor and patentee, who then returned to America...All who have made the leg since, or are making it now, have been my pupils...'

Also chronicled are new wrist movements and elbow joints, 'the quality...regulated by the price patient can afford to pay for finish. It can be made very nice, everything of the best...if the patient will go to the expense'. A wide range of implements to be used as hand substitutes are shown, and the part of the business dealing with replacements for mutilated hands had increased largely. An array of Hospital, French, double spring and American pattern crutches, plus arm slips, padded bandages, and appliances for disunited fractures round off a fascinating glimpse into the past.

Another 136-page booklet is devoted to surgical and abdominal belts for both sexes, trusses, corsets, bust bodices, elastic hosiery, wrestling supports, suspensory bandages, ear caps and chin straps, and is dated 1930 (still in use in 1935), but the illustrations are Edwardian and the fact that all goods were made to order endorses the conviction that Chas., like his competitors, was snapping up little considered trifles, while energetically pursuing every opening for new business. The next catalogues do speak of a 'Blatchford' leg and of experience gained in supplying over twenty thousand limbs to disabled men, backed by more than 40 years' solid manufacturing knowledge. With over 80 different models made by the third decade of this century, we are now in a different era.

Artificial arms and hands

Over two thousand years before the Blatchford arm vied with its Carnes counterpart for general acceptance during the First World War, the Roman historian Pliny tells of another war, in which Marcus Sergius lost his right hand some time between 218 and 202 BC, and was fitted with an iron hand which he used to wield his warrior sword. After this, history, although not rich in information, does show that at least by AD 1400 the problem of apparatus for the upper limb had been the subject of serious study. Some commentators mention patients in the 1580s with forearm amputations, whose replacement was not only ornamental but also highly useful. These had the essentials of any good tool – resistance to force, good grasp and simple mechanism. Moreover, some attempt was made from the fifteenth to seventeenth centuries to help the manual labourer and cripple. The iron apparatus supplied to one man who had lost both hands enabled him to remove his hat, sign his name and open and shut his purse.

In the Middle Ages artificial arms sometimes repaired the ravages of war. An iron hand with fragments of armour, recovered from the mud in the River Rhine, is analogous to others of Italian manufacture from the fifteenth century. All show that those who made limbs and orthopaedic apparatus were either the makers of swords and cuirasses or else they could not escape the influence of a widespread art form which had achieved great perfection. These artificial hands in complete supine form and with rudimentary grasp, could have been used only for horseback riding and the management of bulky objects. They are heavy working hands, with a solid thumb and fingers firmly soldered to a single metal cylinder.

The great pioneer of substitute mechanism was Ambroise Paré, and one of his artificial hands constructed in Paris in 1550, called 'le petit Lorrain' after the famous locksmith of that name, has acquired historic importance. As with the work of Paré, some of the better examples of the craft in the Museo Stibbert in Florence show mechanical hands and fingers worked by springs, ratchets and catches, the flexion graded in six stages.

The iron replacement made for the Teutonic knight Goetz von Berlichingen (1480–1562), who lost his hand in his twenties during the siege of Landshut in Bavaria, was an imaginative piece of machinery. He said that 'It had rendered more service in the fight than ever did the original flesh'. Goetz had several hands made with movable joints and fingers capable of closure, and copies exist of German manufacture, with modified thumb and finger actions. Four of the Goetz adaptions had a

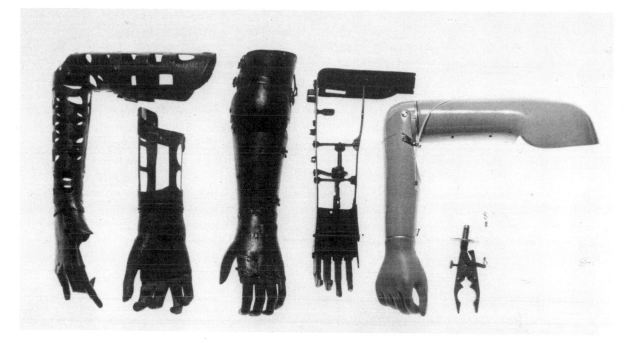

FROM LEFT TO RIGHT: Early 16th-century iron right arm and hand, flexible at elbow and wrist and pierced to make it lighter; 16th-century iron forearm and hand; iron artificial left hand, with fixed thumb but movable fingers; one of several arms made for the warlike German knight, Goetz von Berlichingen; and a more modern prosthesis, plus an alternative terminal device.

rigid thumb, which limits the use of the hand but gives instead a security and simplifies the construction of a working grasp.

A century later an artificial hand was worn by Christian, Duke of Brunswick, but so far as development was concerned the Middle Ages was a period of the big sleep. Appliances were simply rough types of implements which poorer people could make for themselves and are little different from those portrayed on antique mosaics and vases. Any major advances in prosthetic devices were largely due to advances in amputative surgery.

In 1818 a Berlin dentist, Peter Baliff, introduced the use of the trunk and shoulder girdle muscles as a source of power to flex or extend the fingers. The Baliff invention was designed for forearm amputations for which no elbow-flexing mechanism was needed. Another Berliner, the instrument maker Karoline Eichler, developed Baliff's principle for new hands, but reversed it, so that normal extension was maintained by spiral springs, while flexion was upheld by catgut cords, controlled by the opposite shoulder.

Catgut cords attached at the upper end to a special corset behind the sound shoulder and inserted into the back of the artificial forearm was the invention of a Dutch sculptor, van Peeterssen, to permit elbow flexion for above-elbow amputations. Other cords extended the spring-closed fingers on extension or abduction of the arm. The drawback to all these innovations is that catgut cords are not particularly durable.

Considering the infinite complexity of the

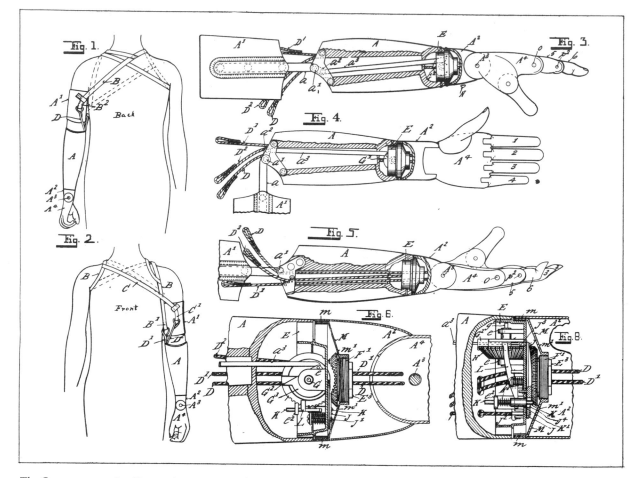

The Carnes arm, a significant advance on anything devised before the First World War.

functions of the human hand, amputation of the arm presents a set of problems as difficult to solve as those presented by leg amputations. This being so, mechanical movements of the artificial arm and hand were extensively developed throughout the last century, and much ingenuity was expended on the design of mechanical hands. Results were reasonably satisfactory, but it was always understood that much development was needed before the artificial hand could

possibly replace even a few of the appliances which could be substituted for it.

A single, crude hand by Claesen, produced in 1886, was the first attempt at an artificial hand which could grasp a heavy object. It anticipated by some 20 years the chief stimulus to the production of mechanical movements – the legendary Carnes arm. Much vaunted from 1904 onwards, this clever appliance introduced a wonderful life-like imitation of flexion of the elbow. It was accompanied by supination of the forearm at the wrist so that the palm of the hand could be brought to the mouth or face. One of the greatest inventions of its kind ever made, it

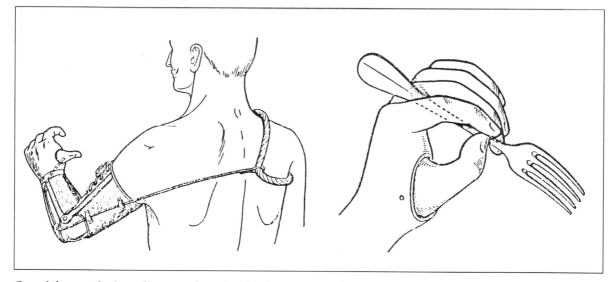

One of the more basic appliances perhaps, but for the new amputee, essential for communication and eating.

The automatic thumb is opened by movement of the sound shoulder and flexion of the thumb, and pressure of the thumb against the side of the middle finger allows a fork or pen to be used.

was, however, costly, and, because of its gears mechanism, heavy (16–24 oz), although the arm as a whole was fairly light. The fingers when closed became locked as in a hand grip, and were therefore more resistant than hands which depended upon springs for assistance to extension.

As discussed in E. Muirhead Little's book, *Artificial Limbs and Amputation Stumps* (1922), British manufacturers offered a range of workers' arms and show arms, which had developed movements and were therefore called mechanical arms. All arms, however ingenious and apparently perfect, had as a rule detachable forearms and hands, so that other appliances could be fitted as and when required. These substitutes were innumerable; the only apparent difficulty lay in the selection of those suitable for individual workers. Possibly too many of these had been devised for, as the author points out, 'a visit to a workshop, where a large number of one-armed men are employed, shows that, as a rule, only single appliances are used'. For special work, however, implements of a more elaborate nature were often useful.

Dress arms are shaped like a normal arm, the forearm and hand not detachable. Metal parts were made of steel or duralumin, the sheaths or shaped parts were made of duralumin, leather or certalmid, a very light and strong composition of fabric and glue, created in the experimental workshops of the Ministry of Pensions during the First World War. As Blatchfords moved from a war footing to peacetime operations, a stream of products in keeping with the state of the art poured from its workshops.

CHAPTER FOUR

The First World War

If health care is seen as an expression of national mood, the overall impression is that in the years leading up to the First World War there was very little solicitude for the limbless. Obviously there was concern for individual cases and private pain, but no alarm at official level. When war broke out in August 1914, the manufacture of artificial limbs was an industry little known in the United Kingdom – cosy, cloistered and best shuffled out of public gaze. Makers were few and demand small.

As is its wont, war acted as a stimulus, and it provoked the invention, improvement and production of artificial limbs. Throughout the war ingenious methods of producing make-shift limbs were devised by prisoners of war utilising crutches or wood and leather discards, but on a universal front, the Great War yielded an experience in the creation and fitting of scientific prostheses unique in history. The storm of battle, however, made it impossible for amputations to be made always on set lines, if as much of the limb as possible was to be saved. Inevitably, the scars and flaps covering the stump were more tender than for ordinary amputations, so that the fitting of prostheses was more difficult in military than in civilian practice, where there was continuity of treatment, prolonged obser-vation and a degree of counselling to keep alight the patient's spirit and resilience.

It was not until the war that special amputee centres were established where surgical and prosthetic care could be given to the wounded. In these centres surgeon and limb maker met at the 'bedside' of the patient, prior to the amputation, to discuss optimum sites and the post-operative management of the patient. Both were concerned to select and fabricate the best limb possible to suit particular needs. But the present close integration of medical and technical resources lay many unbearable months away, and evolved from the early arrangements made by the Ministry of Pensions and other organisations faced with a rush of heavy casualties. Meanwhile, some notion of the chaos faced by the embattled Allies can be gleaned from an article in the *Cartoon Journal* (September 1923):

When thousands upon thousands of disabled limbless men were being discharged from the army, the problems of their disability and future was one of grave difficulty. At this time the supply of artificial limbs to British disabled was largely in the hands of American firms. There has been a certain amount of criticism regarding this state of affairs, but it has to be remembered that limbs were required in numbers undreamt of in pre-war days, and America, being out of the war at this time, alone could supply artificial limbs in sufficient numbers. Of the few British makers, the greater part were working in a small way and entirely lacking in both capacity and initiative. Practically a new industry had been created by the war, and the old fashioned limb maker, working like a cobbler in a little back room, was quite unequal to the occasion. Further, the demands of the army called every available man to the colours, and it was dire necessity that placed our limbless men in the hands of American limb makers.

The French Red Cross were the first to react positively to the crisis effect of scything machine gun fire and shrapnel, which left demand for limbs far outstripping capacity. They were also the quickest to appreciate that manpower and sophisticated limbs were on tap in the United States. Little wonder, then, that as the limb makers' Rupert Brooke-like exhilaration of God having matched them for this hour continued to diminish, those in charge looked elsewhere. They found westward, lo, the land was bright, the Yanks were coming, a full two years before the first American fighting contingents arrived at the front. Two of the leading Yanks in question were the colourful William Edgar 'Billy' Isle, General Manager of J. F. Rowley Inc., and Rowley himself.

The introduction of American legs was not so revolutionary in Britain as it was in France, for British manufacturers had been accustomed to make the stump socket out of a single piece of willow for years. What American innovation provided was:

(a) the use of a sling which passed over the shoulders and attached to the leg below the knee so as to act as a mechanism for extending the knee;

(b) the manufacture of the leg portion out of a single piece of wood;

(c) abolition of the old tendon action for the ankle joint, and its replacement by the ankle with movement limited by india rubber buffers;

(d) the wooden part of the limb covered with a layer of raw hide or parchment, so adding to its strength.

No one wishes to profit from pain, but it can be readily appreciated that as the first crescendo of casualties reached British shores, horizons opened for anyone prepared to capitalise upon a situation which, as it unfolded, grew worse. Nothing in history had conditioned the nation for the stream of shattered men, and it is almost impossible, looking back now, to understand how deep the shock of the war was to go. In the first months of warfare, during the last lingering moments of an era when principles of civilisation, decency and honour were supposed to hold, before war without mercy or scruple engulfed every citizen, limbless men had no option but to return home or to friends, there to await delivery of their limbs by rail or post, and in the meantime manage as best as they could.

Humanity dictated that this haphazard process should not be allowed to last. The need for an elaborate organisation to administer the manufacture, supply, repair and renewal of limbs gradually dawned upon what was still in essence a classbound and slumbering society. And where in this morass was Chas. A. Blatchford? Ever the quicksilver opportunist, and by now a seasoned veteran in the trade and shrewd analyst of the limitations of the domestic market, Chas. must have foreseen that in a highly charged and volatile situation lay the making of the company.

Blatchfords already had a civilian clientele which kept things ticking over, but not to shirk the issue, armament kings are not alone in prospering from the impact of war. With hindsight, Chas's known practicality was laced with a good measure of luck in that he was in the right place at the right time with a

War casualties at the Roehampton Limb Fitting Centre.

NAME	Rate of Pension.	Regiment.	When admitted a Pensioner.	When last supplied with a substitute for a Leg.
Blaney John	*1/*	*46th*	*10 July 1855*	*4 years ago 1863*

who applies for a *Substitute for a Leg*, is required to furnish the following particulars, viz. :—

                                 ANSWERS.

Whether for a *Right or Left Leg*, and whether *above or below the knee.*

IF ABOVE THE KNEE,

State the exact measure round the upper part of the naked stump, close to the fork, not very tight (as A) - - - -

The exact length of the remaining leg from the fork to the ground (from B to C) - -

IF BELOW THE KNEE,

The width of the opening to receive the knee (D) - -

The length from the knee (when turned up) to the ground (E F), which may be ascertained by kneeling on a chair of sufficient height to make both legs of equal length.

Above the Knee Right Leg $\frac{18}{31\frac{1}{2}}$ *Leather*

N.B.—The required measures must be sent in *Writing*; and not by Strips of Paper or String; and must be taken next to the bare Skin. All directions must be plainly written and inserted in this printed Form, or in one similarly drawn up in Writing.

The Out-Pensioners will not be supplied with a substitute for a leg above the knee, or *bucket*, oftener than once in *four years*; nor with a substitute for a leg below the knee, or *box*, oftener than once in *three years*. And it is to be observed that even at the expiration of these periods, the articles will not be supplied unless absolutely required.

Here state, as plainly as possible, the Address in full to which the parcel is to be forwarded.

Name - - -
Address - - - *Commissioners Branch*
County - - -
Nearest Post Town -

I certify that the Applicant is the Pensioner above described, and that he is in need of the article specified in the above Requisition.

26 May 1867.
Examined

R. J. O'Brien Major
Staff Officer of Pensioners
for the *W. London* District.

In the Seaton

Every Victorian war amputee had a free replacement limb by right, no matter how casual to the modern observer its supply and fitting appear.

competent workforce, his own breezy inspiration bolstered by two adult sons prepared to match his own enterprise. Both Tom and W.A. were inventive and energetic young men, precluded from active service by their reserved occupation, but able to give a lead to a staff numbering upwards of fifty or so.

With all statistical data lost on the dusty shelf of yesterday's happenings, we can only guess what percentage of damaged men turned up metaphorically on the doorstep of 90 Clapham Road. Of these a large proportion had to return for re-fitting within six months or a year, not because the limbs were defective or fitted prematurely, but because the stump altered both naturally or as a result of pressure from the socket. The artificial legs made by makers such as Blatchfords were expected to last about seven years, with a call-back period of eight months. The turn-around time for arms was much shorter. The longest an arm had been in use was one year and many of the men destined to come back to Roehampton within the normal six months were those who used them for extraordinarily hard work.

Whereas civilians afflicted by surgical, accidental or natural processes had to look to their own resources, in England arrangements had been in force for many years whereby every soldier and sailor who lost a limb through injury or disease while on active service had the right to expect not just a peg leg – unless by way of a temporary substitute – but a full artificial leg. These were supplied at state expense by the Admiralty, War Office or via Greenwich Hospital (all up to a cost of about £15). Where the cost exceeded the government allowance, a case for a subsidy in part-payment could be made out.

Economic interests were subordinate to the satisfaction of the patient, and to ensure durability and decency, no limb could possibly be priced as low as £5, as was argued in certain – non-trade! – quarters. Owing to the enormous demand, the earliest patients during the war were only fitted with one limb, but following pressure from the Governors of Roehampton Hospital, medical staff and concerned Members of Parliament, provisional spare limbs were supplied so that the amputee was never without one. The value of the provisional limb lay in its acting as a kind of 'slipper', and as a reserve in case of accident to the mechanical one.

Officers who lost a leg were also fitted with an artificial one free of charge and given a wound pension of £100 per annum, out of which they were expected to defray repair and renewal expenses. This was in addition to retired pay, so that no officer who lost a leg in action got less, in the aggregate, than £150 p.a. By August 1919 regulations about the cost of repairs and renewals through fair wear and tear were extended to retired officers. The second mechanical limb might be obtained under Article 647 of the Pay Warrant or be provided by one of the special limb-fitting hospitals, working in collaboration with a Red Cross provisional limbs depot established in the neighbourhood. Army Council Instruction No. 786 of 1916 fixed a scale of prices for the various types of limb, varying from £10.10s. for a Syme's amputation to £29.8s. for an ordinary leg with a pelvic band or £40 for an arm of complex type for use in special cases.

These figures are intriguing, since all Blatchfords' financial records for 1914–18 have perished. An hypothesis can be made that even if routine repair charges are *excluded*, as well as the cost of spare and substitute limbs already mentioned, and Blatchfords' share of over 40,000 limbless ex-servicemen is calculated at a mere 8 per cent, then, allowing an average price of £20

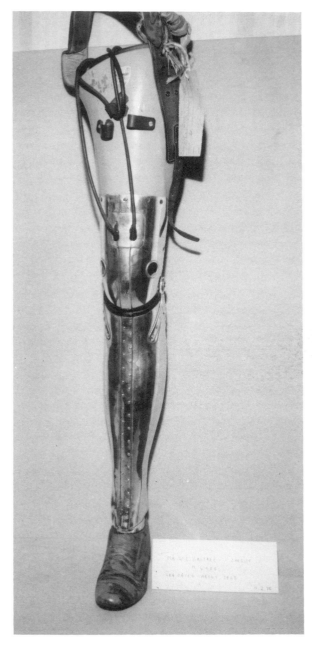

The 'New Blatchford' leg connected the false limb to the living flesh 'as though part of it'.

per case, the income from London and Cardiff might have been in the order of £65,000; something like £1.6m by today's standards. Taking all other factors into consideration, a figure double that might be nearer the mark.

E. W. Gower's invaluable compilation, *Queen Mary's Hospital and Limb Fitting Centre* (1965) shows how private enterprise took a hand while bureaucracy floundered, with the foundation and development of what was originally hoped would be the national venue for all cases of amputations and special orthopaedic cases. Largely the original concept of the indomitable Mrs Gwynne Holford, the Queen Mary's Convalescent Auxiliary Hospitals were founded on 11 May 1915. It was Mrs Holford who, with Lady Falmouth and the first Secretary/Treasurer, Sir Charles Kenderdine, a London estate agent, raised considerable sums for the treatment and reception of limbless ex-servicemen. In idyllic surroundings they were supplied with the best known artificial appliances and instructed in their use.

To get the hospital off the ground, Kenneth Wilson lent Roehampton House, near Barnes in south-west London, and J. Pierpont Morgan the adjoining Dover House, together capable of accommodating three hundred officers and men. A grant was made from the National Relief Fund and eminent physicians and orthopaedic surgeons attended clinics daily and in the evenings. A temporary hut was constructed in the grounds of the hospital at a cost of £250, half of which was borne by J. F. Rowley, who shared with Blatchfords the miniscule fitting rooms. This was swiftly expanded into a plant capable of multiple production of prostheses, given or rented to the same two firms early in 1916. A personal note on 'Billy' Isle in the *Orthopaedic and Prosthetic Appliance Journal* (June 1959) gives details of the recruitment of skilled British woodworkers and American prosthetists until the staff grew to more than a hundred.

Workshops were set up for the assembly of imported components, and a quota of over seventy limbs a week enabled the same number of men to pass through the hospital in good time.

Rowley and Company (taken over by Hangers in 1926), led by Isle, were in occupation, having with J. E. Hanger Inc. and Carnes Artificial Limb Company made the lucrative trans-Atlantic passage in 1915 and picked up the major contracts, so that American domination was almost complete. English firms of repute were engaged in making artificial limbs in competition with the Americans, and representatives of the small number of London companies called on the Hospital Superintendent for orders. Familiar names such as W. R. Grossmith, Masters and Son, Charles Salmon and Sons, Horace V. Duncan, Anderson and Whitelaw joined Chas. A. Blatchford & Sons, followed shortly afterwards by Desoutter Brothers and, in 1921, by Hugh Steeper.

Outside the Roehampton orbit, several other manufacturers rushed to do their bit, frequently with an advertising fuss and furore unknown to Blatchfords. Albert E. Evans of Fitzroy Square, London, made 'every aid to enable war crippled men to resume work and become useful citizens', while J. & E. Ferris claimed contractual relations to the War Office, the Admiralty, and Canadian and Anzac countries. When it came to publicity however, no one maintained a higher profile than F. G. Ernst. It was rare for the quality end of the medical press to notice artificial limbs as a fit topic for editorial comment, which makes *The Lancet* of 8 December 1917 singular. It reviewed what it described as a 'well published and printed quarto book of 60 pages', in which the mechanical action, not only of artificial limbs, but also of numerous accessories enabling the wearer to dress himself, shave, smoke, hold a pen, play billiards, handle coins and attend to lavatory requirements, is laid out in clear language, diagrams and photographs. It went on to say: 'The need which has been created as a result of war has inevitably stimulated the invention, improvement, and production of artificial limbs, and medical men would find the catalogue issued by Mr. F. G. Ernst, orthopaedic mechanician to the National Orthopaedic Hospital and other institutions, invaluable.'

No such 'plug' came Blatchfords' way, though it might have come in handy in the jockeying for pole position against the almighty US import, exemplified by the Carnes arm. Whereas today Blatchfords' sole concern is with artificial legs, throughout the 1914–18 war the Blatchford arm was the company's flag carrier, although the crafting of other products continued unabated. The Carnes arm was a formidable rival, and there were occasions in the middle of the long, hard slog when damage limitation exercises were called for.

A Parliamentary Question of 15 April 1918 probably left in its wake cause for rueful contemplation (and fierce lobbying?). This was when a Colonel Ashley asked the Pensions Minister whether 'in view of the general opinion held by discharged soldiers who had lost an arm that the Carnes arm was in most cases preferable to the Blatchford arm, would steps be taken to issue such an arm in suitable cases'. Colonel Gibbs (on behalf of the Minister) smoothly replied in the best 'Yes, Minister' tradition that he had to be guided by expert orthopaedic surgeons, and a Carnes arm was supplied in all cases where specially recommended by the surgeons in charge of the case. A delightfully opaque answer, one feels, leaving an equal number of questions unanswered and unanswerable.

For all that, ideas literally poured out of Clapham Road – five known patent applications lodged in 1917 alone, six the next year. Looking at them over 70 years later, the present Technical

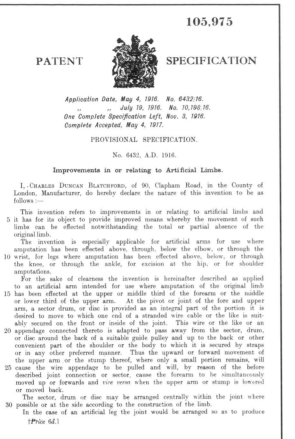

105,975

PATENT **SPECIFICATION**

Application Date, May 4, 1916. No. 6432/16.
,,   ,,   July 19, 1916. No. 10,198/16.
One Complete Specification Left, Nov. 3, 1916.
Complete Accepted, May 4, 1917.

PROVISIONAL SPECIFICATION.

No. 6432, A.D. 1916.

Improvements in or relating to Artificial Limbs.

I,·CHARLES DUNCAN BLATCHFORD, of 90, Clapham Road, in the County of
London, Manufacturer, do hereby declare the nature of this invention to be as
follows :—

This invention refers to improvements in or relating to artificial limbs and
5 it has for its object to provide improved means whereby the movement of such
limbs can be effected notwithstanding the total or partial absence of the
original limb.
The invention is especially applicable for artificial arms for use where
amputation has been effected above, through, below the elbow, or through the
10 wrist, for legs where amputation has been effected above, below, or through
the knee, or through the ankle, for excision at the hip, or for shoulder
amputations.
For the sake of clearness the invention is hereinafter described as applied
to an artificial arm intended for use where amputation of the original limb
15 has been effected at the upper or middle third of the forearm or the middle
or lower third of the upper arm.   At the pivot or joint of the fore and upper
arm, a sector drum, or disc is provided as an integral part of the portion it is
desired to move to which one end of a stranded wire cable or the like is suit-
ably secured on the front or inside of the joint.   This wire or the like or an
20 appendage connected thereto is adapted to pass away from the sector, drum,
or disc around the back of a suitable guide pulley and up to the back or other
convenient part of the shoulder or the body to which it is secured by straps
or in any other preferred manner.   Thus the upward or forward movement of
the upper arm or the stump thereof, where only a small portion remains, will
25 cause the wire appendage to be pulled and will, by reason of the before
described joint connection or sector, cause the forearm to be simultaneously
moved up or forwards and *vice versa* when the upper arm or stump is lowered
or moved back.
The sector, drum or disc may be arranged centrally within the joint where
30 possible or at the side according to the construction of the limb.
In the case of an artificial leg the joint would be arranged so as to produce

†*Price 6d.*]

Front of the first Blatchford Patent Application.

and Marketing Director John Shorter was
quietly staggered by the fertility of invention
shown by Chas. and Tom, working in tandem,
as well as the range and diversity of their
thinking. The first surviving patent application
was formally submitted by Tom on 4 May 1916,
and a patent granted the same day a year later.
Like all its fellows, number 105,975 was adroitly
handled by Patent Agents J. S. Withers and
Spooner. It provided a suitable clutch or locking
means at the joint or pivot of the elbow (though
with equal potential for the knee), making it
possible to control the elbow lock without the

use of the other hand to manipulate the joint 'as
at present where locking joints are provided'.

Just over six months later, thought was given
to a pad applied under the sound arm of the
wearer to reduce the discomfort and chaffing
caused by the bands or straps to control
movements of the artificial arm and hand.
Furthermore, in February 1917, meticulous
details cover an elbow joint, and with it a device
for fitting tools to artificial limbs via an
attachment plate to be secured into a plate
provided at the end of the socket piece carrying
the stump of the upper arm. Subsequent
modifications touched on devices for securing to
the upper arm or hook attachments for holding
knives, forks and other implements, but that the
company exerted itself in other directions is
shown by the earliest patent leg specification in
the company's archives. This was filed by Chas.
on 9 February 1917, and provided an artificial
leg with ball-bearing knee and ankle joints,
comprising side plates secured to said limb
members, a spindle supporting the plates, a
fastening sleeve and self-contained anti-friction
bearings interposed between the spindle and
sleeve.

The stimulus of war led to swift advances in
design, and mechanical knee joints, ankle joints
and other innovations bearing on the skill of
walking were the subject of constant Blatchford
experiment and research. On 9 November 1917,
Chas. offered for approval a simple and
inexpensive Central Knee Control (CKC) device,
whereby the lower leg or calf member of an
artificial leg could be returned to a supporting
position after having moved backward when
walking, or when the wearer had been sitting,
'thus ensuring a degree of noiseless operation
and positive safety'. The *following day*
imaginative minds had come up with an
improved, simple and (again) inexpensive ankle
joint designed to minimise shocks when the
wearer is walking up and down hill. Scores more

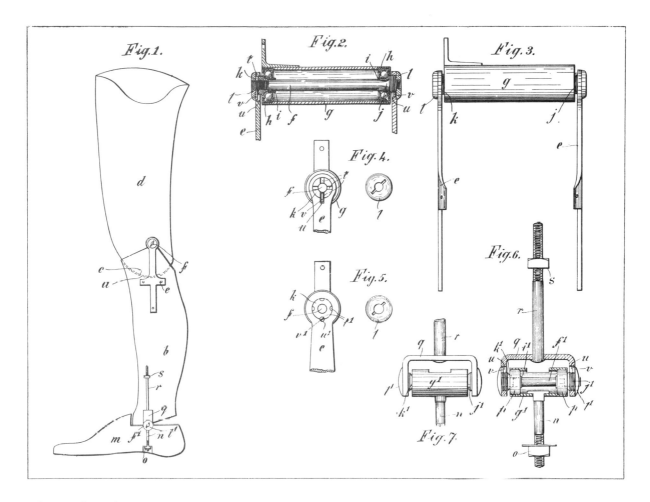

ideas reflected post-war adaptation to the light metal limb as well as Blatchfords' traditional skill in working with wood.

At a meeting of the Medical Society of London in October 1917, many of the appliances manufactured by Adams, Blatchfords, Hobbs and Anderson were on show on the arms worn by the men present. Major R. C. Elmslie, a household name in orthopaedic surgery at the time, pointed out many of them as typical examples of work done at Roehampton and elsewhere. Quick detachability, other than by the screw method, was ideal, and new ideas

A significant development in the company's history of designs, this drawing for a ball-bearing joint, filed in 1917, represents its first patent for lower limbs.

were always forthcoming. As far as arms were concerned, Elmslie was pleased to point out the manifest and immense mechanical advance upon the very elementary types available at the beginning of the war.

Design under duress concentrates the mind, and Elmslie, very much a senior member of the surgical staff at Queen Mary's Hospital, would be among those best placed to recall the

War casualties at Roehampton learning to use their newly fitted limbs.

critically important International Exhibition of artificial limbs held at Roehampton back in July 1915. About 24 firms, many of them American, and one or two Scandinavian, participated, and among those invited to this public forum was Blatchfords. The Directors-General of the Navy and Army Medical Services, together with the President of the Royal College of Surgeons of England and a committee of English, Scottish and Irish surgeons, judged the exhibits with an eye to deciding what appliances should be adopted as standard patterns. The medals were offered by Mrs Gwynne Holford and Sir Charles Kenderdine, and the gold for best general excellence went to the Chicago firm of J. F. Rowley. Its General Manager in the United Kingdom, 'Billy' Isle was irresistible. He had only recently undergone amputation after a railway accident, but his philosophy of 'it's not what you've lost that counts, it's what you have left' enabled him to run the length of the hall, move freely up and down stairs, dance and jump to demonstrate the adaptability of his company's leg. All else paled by comparison, but W. R. Grossmith managed to pick up the silver medal in the same class.

The gold medal for the greatest advance in mechanism was given to the arm exhibited by the Carnes Artificial Limb Company of Kansas City. It was attached to the middle of the humerus in such a way that the wearer had the finesse even to pluck out a hair. The silver in this section was awarded to another old-established firm, Mayer and Meltzer of London, for a leg, opening laterally, of simple mechanism, and easily adjustable by the wearer. Others subsequently honoured included Chas. A. Blatchford & Sons.

The carnage since August 1914 had been grave and the number of amputations great, hence this assembly of all the talents, but there was a long, long trail of wounded men yet to unwind, and by November 1916 there were 2,400 cases on the Hospital Register at Queen Mary's and 1,250 patients ready or nearly ready to be admitted. Long delays in fitting artificial limbs often led to wasting of the muscles and loss of strength, and on this account Roehampton was doing an invaluable service by ensuring limb fitting as soon as the stump was ready for it. To cope with demand for more and more beds, by February 1918 four other hospitals had been established, two each in Scotland and Ireland, deliberately sited near to cities such as Edinburgh and Dublin so that orthopaedic surgeons on the consulting staffs might be in close attendance. Five more were planned, including a second one in London, the 5th London T.F. Hospital, perhaps better known as St Thomas's Hospital. June that year witnessed many complaints by suffering men about delays causing pain, anxiety and financial loss. The difficulty was not always so much that of priority beds, but rather of the continued shortage of limb fitters who could turn out limbs of approved pattern and of securing the services of surgeons who were specialists in limb work.

The fitting centre for the whole of Wales was at the Prince of Wales's Hospital in Cardiff, an exclusive preserve of Blatchfords for some years after 1916, and managed by W. A. with a tact and *savoir-faire* which masked his quiet disposition and youth. A parliamentary rumble in February 1918 that having one centre in Wales necessitated an unwonted amount of expenditure, and loss of time for an increasing number of cases, was not his affair, just one more footnote to bureaucracy at war.

Very much on the lines of Queen Mary's Hospital, Roehampton, its workshops equipped with electrical appliances, lathes and a model motor chassis, these hospitals readily dispensed moral support, guidance, ancillary nursing services, sport and recreational facilities for war-numbed men. At a certain stage resumption of work is the best therapy, and the authorities were slow to accept that delaying re-education until the local condition had become permanent, and until the discharged patient was in receipt of his prosthetic apparatus, was detrimental to morale. Equally critical was their liaison role, undertaken in conjunction with the voluntary services, in finding employment for discharged patients. Large numbers were trained and found situations, but nevertheless over a third had to be passed on to the local committees for employment, and it became common cause for these committees, employers and trade unions to coax – or coerce – all but the minority of hard cases into the recovery of their self-respect and industrial efficiency.

Employment agencies, as set up by Lloyd George in 1912, were still a novelty, and when it became apparent only nine months after the

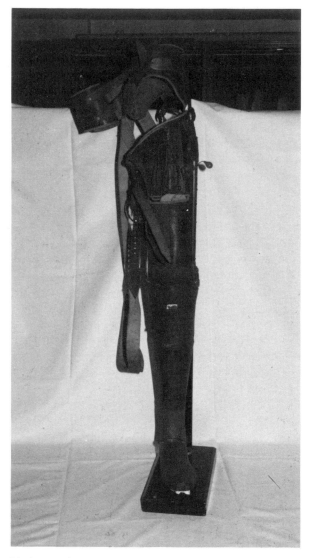

Limb manufacture is international in scope, as shown by a Japanese above-knee limb leather padded socket, made before the Second World War.

and industrially rehabilitated outside of sheltered workshops – if only to free more men for the Front. With this in mind, it soon became an essential ingredient in the re-education of the disabled that form comes after function: 'form is for Sundays and holidays, and function is for workdays'. To deal with the numbers involved and save journey time and inconvenience, a network of centres was started in other towns. It was never the intention that the disabled should depend solely upon the advice, no doubt highly skilled, of the instrument makers, so each centre was staffed by a Roehampton-trained surgeon with administrative back-up, while the contractors provided a branch workshop and fitting accommodation. Manual training centres for those discharged from convalescent homes took up any slack to prevent discouragement and ensure the use of artificial limbs to best economic advantage.

Roehampton remained the parent centre and exemplar in the preparation of men for civil and industrial life. Its workshops grew in size and importance, becoming a centre for design, fitting and post-graduate training, rated by many as unexcelled throughout the world. In 1917, for instance, a research department was set up in the hospital and foremost among its innovations was the development of certalmid, described as a 'laminated plastic material'. Primarily used for arms, but also a feature of leg manufacture, it remained in use until after the Second World War and the advent of true plastics.

Despite the months of frenzied activity – or perhaps because of them – *The Lancet*, in an end-of-term report dated September 1918, felt justified in apportioning blame all round, pausing only to acknowledge the debt owed to the American limb-fitting firms who had answered Britain's cry for help. Making trenchant comment, *The Lancet* pointed out that more attention could have been paid to the mediocre results obtained on artificial arms with

outbreak of war that the casualties in the Dardanelles campaign alone far exceeded the total number of wounded in the Anglo-Boer War, sound economic reasons dictated that men should be cared for, paid a disability pension their variety of hands and alternative appliances. Only after at least a month's instruction in the use of the arm in the correct user-friendly conditions, could an assessment be attempted on the real value of the replacement arms, and the available reports were patchy. Again, the medical profession, local fitters and limb manufacturers, employers and the disabled themselves all ought to be made to understand that limb adjustment from time to time was essential. Since 50 per cent of the disabled were likely to return to hospital for many years to come, random suggestions currently in vogue that men with unsatisfactory limbs should report to their local War Pensions Committee, be seen by a medical referee, and have their repairs done by a local limb fitter, were 'insupportable'.

The Lancet continued that too much vested interest had crept into the limb-fitting industry, and many who described themselves as limb fitters had no real experience of the work, and their reports upon so-called 'defective' limbs were biased and self-centred. Over-intimate relationships with limb makers were uncalled for in that the limbs actually made were as good as any that could be obtained anywhere, while the American type of leg, introduced at Roehampton, was superior to the older English type of tendon leg, a fact those responsible were enjoined to bear in mind.

By 1918 still to be perfected was a satisfactory knee mechanism which would lock in any degree of flexion when a strain was placed upon it, so that the wearer felt stable when his weight came upon the flexed knee. Inventions in trial stages gave hope for a solution. The British official prostheses represented the accumulated experience not just of the present conflict but of all wars, but finality had not yet been reached. A single, standardised pattern of artificial leg had yet to be adopted, as no specimen of limb brought to the attention of the expert advisory council had shown such advantage over any

others as to warrant it being made the formula pattern. There also remained the problem of the type of material to be used in its construction.

Much controversy had centred around the weight of artificial legs. Making every allowance for the difficulties during the war and for the extent of the artificial limb problem generally, suspicion lingers that much valuable time was lost over the introduction of limbs lighter in weight, and a situation was allowed to develop which might have been prevented by more business-like methods in the Artificial Limb Department of the Ministry of Pensions, and which was to prompt a spirited correspondence in *The Times* of December 1920. Overall distribution of weight is even more important than the total weight, a point succinctly put by one patient: 'When the socket fits me properly the limb feels no weight at all, but when it is too loose it seems to weigh a ton.' Prostheses for the leg can never be too light, provided they are strong enough, and light metal limbs made of duralumin were just coming into use at the beginning of the war.

The metal artificial limb created in the rear of his engineering premises by Charles Desoutter for his amputee brother, Marcel, a former test pilot, won widespread approval on account of its lightness and mechanical ingenuity. Similar limbs made of aluminium and leather were asked for by so many handicapped persons that before the end of 1913 Desoutter Brothers was formed to manufacture them. They were reckoned to be immeasurably superior to the wooden legs which were then the main source of supply, but the price, £100 or more in 1917, placed them out of reach of thousands of legless ex-servicemen. At St Thomas's Hospital, a massage school specialising in Swedish Remedial Exercises already existed, and many ways were devised by the 'physotherapeutic' department of helping in the management of artificial limbs, which 'As officially issued

...were heavy and unwieldy, and the [Sister] was convinced that lighter limbs would give a greater degree of control. She won over the Treasurer...and money was made available for light-weight limbs to be purchased by the *hospital* [my italics], until it was possible to persuade the Ministry of Pensions that the dearer aluminium limb was worth the expense, because it was easier to manipulate than a wooden one' (*St. Thomas' Hospital*, 1914–48, pp. 162–3).

The Committee of Enquiry on Artificial Limbs appointed by the Minister of Pensions, Ian MacPherson, having listened to expert opinion from surgeons, representative limb fitters and wearers of various limbs, decided in favour of the Desoutter metal limb as the prototype of thousands supplied to disabled servicemen, once the question of cost was overcome. It was not until the 1920s, however, that a light metal limb with a wooden socket was made available by the Ministry to those patients who had short thigh stumps or other conditions demanding a particularly short limb.

CHAPTER FIVE

Ups and Downs

Once the thunder of the guns was stilled, quiet contemplation of the hectic period of trial and error produced by war unfolded the relative paramountcy not of the Blatchford leg, but of the Blatchford arm. A letter from Major General i/c the Royal Hospital, Chelsea, written on 26 July 1916 to the Secretary at the War Office, firmly states that 'the majority of artificial arms have been supplied by Mr. C.A.Blatchford, an English maker, who gave up the supply of legs expressly to enable him to cope with the demand for arms'.

Statistics produced by a subcommittee of the Advisory Council on Artificial Limbs late in 1918 were based on arms made by two makers only: Messrs Blatchford and Anderson & Whitelaw, 'due of course to the larger output of these firms consequent upon the general facilities offered by them, and also to the fact that their products meet with the approval of the surgeons in the limited field for selection...'. Such small numbers were supplied by other British firms that they could not be relied upon in any quality comparison. Blatchfords were thus one of the largest suppliers, producing almost 20 times as many arms as legs. Orders given by the Royal Hospital, Chelsea, to Blatchfords for artificial limbs for Roehampton patients up to July 1916, refer to 33 legs ordered and the number not yet reported passed as nil, as against 628 arms on order and 77 yet to be passed.

Hearkening back again to July 1916, the Committee on Artificial Limbs enjoyed a demonstration of an arm made by Blatchfords, during which a patient showed off a variety of contemporary accessories, such as a vice, fork, plus an array of tools. An axe was wielded to good effect and the wood so chopped, then shaped and turned by disabled carpenters. Frequency of repairs at Roehampton, too, showed Blatchfords to advantage in 1916. The returns rate was as low as 3 per cent for legs, and arms a mere 0.98 per cent. The percentages for Hangers was 8.08 per cent, Rowley 8.46 per cent and Ernst 10.09 per cent.

However, as a successful major producer under war-time conditions, when any work was particularly stressful, Blatchfords found themselves in the invidious position of being there to be shot at, their many satisfied customers discounted and ignored. Without ever mentioning names, certain Honourable Members who espoused the cause of the disabled held that the majority of men supplied with artificial arms and appliances found them relatively useless, or useful only for the sake of appearance. Labourers and skilled men used them most, but the mechanism was inadequate

Roehampton Hospital, 1917; a soldier learns how to use an artificial arm.

and the springs too weak. The unsatisfactory character of the limbs was frequently pointed out to the manufacturers. Blatchfords were not unmindful of what was to be an on-going problem for years, and in a brochure printed some time in the late 1920s they candidly accepted that, in the search for the ideal, of some 50 designs of mechanical hands patented in the United Kingdom within the previous few years none had been permanently successful. It was impossible to reproduce the action of the human

hand, and the company itself 'in recent years' had designed four different types, but they were simply devices for opening and closing movements, and their limited mobility caused patients often to discard them.

Nevertheless, by the end of the war limb manufacturers were glutted with work and could virtually dictate the pace of output. In September 1918, for instance, there were 4,000 cases outstanding which required fitment of artificial arms, and in a letter to Sir Charles Kenderdine, the Minister of Pensions hints at the strength of their position: 'I have now had replies from all the arm making limbmakers to two months later the British group rode the tide and asked for a general increase of 25 per cent on prices for most limbs and 33 per cent in special cases. Clearly someone had to give, and Whitehall rarely does.

A Departmental Committee on Artificial Limbs was appointed on 14 February 1919, and among those asked to report as witnesses were the Chairman of the Limbmakers Association and spokesmen for Messrs Blatchford, Desoutter, Rowley, Hanger and Grossmith. It was decided that no case had been made for a general increase in prices. A costing expert was to be brought in to examine the accounts of the five firms and the matter was left for due consideration by the new Contracts Department. As part of a proposed control of limb makers and in what reads like a genteel crackdown, the Committee recommended the submission of full and complete accounts and all work was to be subject to Ministry inspection. Minimum wage rates were laid down and employees were to include a fair number of limbless

ABOVE AND RIGHT: Blatchford arms demonstrating their uses.

my enquiry as to the number of arms they can supply without detriment to their present output. The number is about 350 per month at present...'. Short of another giant influx of expensive American manpower, the purchasing authorities were over the proverbial barrel, and

The first soldier to be fitted at the Prince of Wales Hospital with two Blatchford Arms writing a letter after ten days' practice.

Are we Downhearted

NO

Prince of Wales Hospital

Cardiff.   June 30ᵗʰ 1919

J. Collins Thomas 22242.
6ᵗʰ Cameron Highlanders.

An additional testimonial.

men. If a limb was supplied at state expense, the limb maker could offer only the Ministry-approved limb, unless otherwise sanctioned.

It will be remembered that largely as a result of the 1915 Roehampton Exhibition, the Rowley limb knee-control mechanism was adopted by government for the 'standard limb'. The specifications of these limbs were approved by the Advisory Council to the Ministry in August 1920, and in a few months all artificial legs of wood or leather supplied to war pensioners would comply with the new patterns. From the ankle up to the thigh the mechanism of the limb and its metal components were uniform, and capable of being supplied in quantity by engineering firms. The fitting and assembly of the limb itself was to be the preserve of the limb maker, in accordance with his own technique.

Standardisation was not to stand in the way of progress, and the inventions of all manufacturers and their modifications were incorporated into sections of the so-called standard limb. In the lamentable absence of such a being as the standard person, personalised requirements allowed limb makers the final say in subtle expressions of their finesse with, say, ankle joints tailored to give the amount of movement acceptable to the wearer.

A further suggestion from the Committee was that the limb makers themselves should allocate the proportion of arms and legs supplied over the next two to three years, and decentralisation of supply work was also urged, so that some of the makers who had until then concentrated their work in London, should either move to provincial centres or open branch premises there. In what was surely one of the early business incentive schemes, the Committee strongly desired that government should not hesitate to sanction compensation or loans towards the opening of new premises or scrapping of the old.

The first ever regional centre had in fact been set up by Blatchfords at Cardiff in early 1916. A map of England and Wales attached and annotated to a report dated 20 May 1919 suggests that W.A.'s workforce there was enduring a hard slog. With figures such as 'Men, 2092; beds, 55; limbs per week [produced], 20' there was obviously room for another manufacturer in Cardiff.

The nearby Rhondda Valley collieries added their fair quota of industrial injuries and it is symbolic of inter-war priority given to special classes of disabled citizens that no such national arrangements for decentralised limb supply existed for all civilians. Not for them the Ministry code of practice whereby limbs were prescribed by surgeons with special experience, augmented by a supervised follow-up training in their use. As soon as the ordinary hospital patient's stump was healed, he or she was handed over to the almoner, who gave an order to a surgical instrument maker, who might well have been only a middleman as far as artificial limbs were concerned. In due course a limb was made ready and the patient expected to take it away and use it. Too often patients could not manage their limb, and the burden rested with the limb maker to take the hazardous course of sending the case back to the surgeon, the intimation being that the work had been done imperfectly. E. Muirhead Little, at Roehampton, was among the few at this period able to control and modify the empiricism of the limb maker, and in *The Lancet* (4 December 1926) he fulminated against the curtailment of the rights of the ordinary citizen, suggesting that London hospitals emulate Roehampton and establish a limb-fitting centre, in which the prescription, fitting and use of limbs would be carried out under surgical direction.

Some 26 firms were contracted to the Ministry of Pensions, and while British workmanship was second to none, the *British Medical Journal* of 4 December 1926 felt that their work was apt to go uncriticised. Muirhead Little and W.R. Grossmith also took umbrage in print at the exclusion from the hospital custom at Roehampton of all but Hangers and Blatchfords, commenting that patients did not have a perfectly free choice, and that it was not possible to secure the service of Roehampton surgeons bound by their government contracts.

Responsibility for the whole work of supply, repair and renewal of artificial limbs and appliances had been assumed by the Ministry of Pensions under Treasury Authority of 4 July 1917, but not until a policy statement by the Minister of Pensions of 7 October 1919 did the long arm of government finally impose the complete new regime. Standardisation of component parts, such as the Hanger–Blatchford ankle joint (already adopted by the Advisory Council), as well as whole limbs, has already been noted, but for Chas. and his contemporaries reading through the document there was to be a judicious mixture of honey and gall. A number of manufacturers would be appointed limb makers to the Ministry of Pensions but the strings attached would be forceful and binding. A warrant imposed conditions which included:

(a) records of costs were to be kept and inspection of books allowed;

(b) profit margins to be fixed at reasonable levels from time to time by the Ministry on a costing principle;

(c) Ministry representatives to agree exceptional profit because of special improvements/inventions.

The devouring need to *know*, to be witness to the reasoning behind the decision to form Blatchfords into a limited private company on 29 December 1919 is forever lost. The past cannot get up from its grave and parade before our eyes, but a reasonable hypothesis can be made that the last link in an inexorable chain of motive and causation lies in clauses (a) to (c) above. Provision of company records in Britain was then on a wholly voluntary basis, and, unlike the great Victorian railway tycoon, George Hudson, who kept everything except his own accounts, Chas. kept nothing. Now, however, to satisfy systematic investigation, he had to give the company a modern accountancy profile.

Financial fragment from the past: a receipt in connection with extra space at 90 Clapham Road.

Chas. took the chair at the first meeting of directors, held at 7 Portman Street in London's West End, the offices of the company solicitors, Messrs Cooper, Bake, Roche and Fettes. Albert George Fettes, later Company Secretary and Board Director, acted as auditor and was present along with Tom and W.A. The date, 28 May 1920, was seminal in Blatchfords' history in that the Corporate Seal was on that day attached to an agreement between Chas. and the company he founded, for the sale and purchase of the business and assignment of certain assets from himself to his sons.

The principal object of the new company was the continuance of the work carried on by the vendor 'for many years past', and the purchase covered stock in trade, plant and fixtures, loose plant, tools, and full benefit of all current contracts. Stock in trade, plant and fixtures were valued at £7,000, and goodwill and other property assessed at £4,500. The capital sum involved was £10,000, with £2 in cash and the balance by allotment and issue of 9,998 Ordinary Shares of £1 each. Chas. was allotted one share, number 5999, and W.A., number 6000, and, as purchase consideration, numbered shares were given: 1–5998 to Chas., 6001–8000 to Tom, while W.A.'s registered shares were numbered 8001–10,000. In November of that year, share number 6000, of £1, was passed from W.A. to Chas., giving the latter 6,000 in all.

Other than royalties up to a sum of £1,500 due to Tom and W.A., Chas. discharged all corporate liabilities and indemnified his sons against debts and liabilities accruing after the date of the sale. In the presence of the purchasers, the Seal was affixed to an agreement relating to a schedule of 15 patents granted to Chas., the earliest of which was dated 5 December 1916 (No. 111,706, for an arm pad), and the last entry, No. 125,750 of 24 April 1918, refers simply to 'Artificial Leg Improvements'.

A further agreement referred to four existing patents in the names of Tom and W.A. These could be used freely by the new company but

A group of Blatchford limb-wearers.

they could not be assigned and licences could not be granted for outside use. Further inventions or discoveries were exclusive to the company, which would look after fees for their upkeep, although they remained in the names of the inventors. As it happens, Patent Specification No. 105,975, for the 'Original Arm', was credited to Tom and pre-dated by seven months any given to his father.

The engagement of Tom and W.A. as managers of the company rounded off proceedings. In return for a remuneration of £500 per annum each, they were to serve the company for ten years as from 1 July 1920, and in the event of any excess income, they should be paid at the same rate as that hitherto paid to Chas. Payment of the £2 sum mentioned above, and the issue to Chas. and his nominees of the shares stipulated, were made in full by July 1920, and it was confirmed that £4,500 should be regarded as

consideration for the goodwill and the company's patents holdings. In return for the goodwill, an appropriate number of shares, 4,500, were issued to Chas., and to his sons was passed full benefit of the goodwill, patents and improvement rights, all contracts and engagements, plus exclusive use of the name 'Chas. A. Blatchford and Sons'.

A celebratory glass was certainly in order at the first Ordinary General Meeting held at Clapham Road on 29 December 1920, but otherwise it sounds a quiet affair, for pending publication of the first accounts, discussion was held over. The minutes of the next meeting on 30 June 1921, set the tone and format for most subsequent gatherings. Informality was the keynote. Auditors were appointed and

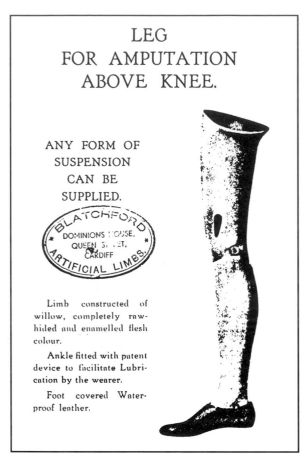

LEG
FOR AMPUTATION
ABOVE KNEE.

ANY FORM OF
SUSPENSION
CAN BE
SUPPLIED.

BLATCHFORD
DOMINIONS HOUSE,
QUEEN STREET,
CARDIFF
ARTIFICIAL LIMBS

Limb constructed of
willow, completely raw-
hided and enamelled flesh
colour.

Ankle fitted with patent
device to facilitate Lubrication by the wearer.

Foot covered Water-
proof leather.

*Leg for amputation above the knee, an illustration from one
of the catalogues.*

reappointed, funds transferred to honour accruing demands and tax liabilities and, primarily, the remuneration of the directors settled. The sums involved oscillated in response to the general trading situation of the company, and, in default of more generous minute-taking, act as a barometer of the firm's changing fortunes. Still buoyed up by the floodtide of ex-service disabled, the company was able to reward its directors' endeavours for the first year by £7,375. 12s.10d, split pro-portionately three ways, climbing in September 1922 to £5,000 for the Chairman and £2,000 each to fellow directors Tom and W.A.

The gradual erosion of the number of war patients is mirrored by the drop in directors' fees to £2,100 the following year, easing upwards by May 1924 to give Chas. £1,450 and £1,025 to each of the brothers. Capture of a slice of the growing private sector became imperative. Queen Mary's (Roehampton) Hospital had become recognised as the premier consultancy centre, and by 1922, with its 18 provincial centres, had handled more than 25,000 primary cases, with attendances for renewals and repairs running into hundreds of thousands. At the same time, the first real reduction in the intake of limbless men began to show, and by 1925 it was clear that the cost of upkeep no longer justified the hospital's primary purpose. Facilities for general, surgical and medical cases were therefore upgraded to meet the needs of a limited number of civilian cases living in or near the capital and treated by arrangement with the London County Council and other bodies. In 1935 the Ministry of Pensions provided more than 4,000 limbs, chiefly in replacement, and repaired more than 35,000. Fears that as the needs of ex-servicemen decreased, the accumulated expertise in war trauma would be denied to groups such as railwaymen and miners, whose work rendered them susceptible to injury, were allayed when the Ministry's limb-fitting services both at Roehampton and at affiliated centres in the provinces were extended in 1936 to embrace the whole population. Funding came from railway companies, local authorities, trade unions, insurance companies and charitable institutions. At the hospital, modern brick buildings superseded the old hutted quarters occupied since 1915 by the limb fitters, offering a more dignified environment for the 800 or so patients admitted annually on a private basis.

Blatchford patient, Ernest Underwood, with the company's refinement of his own invention.

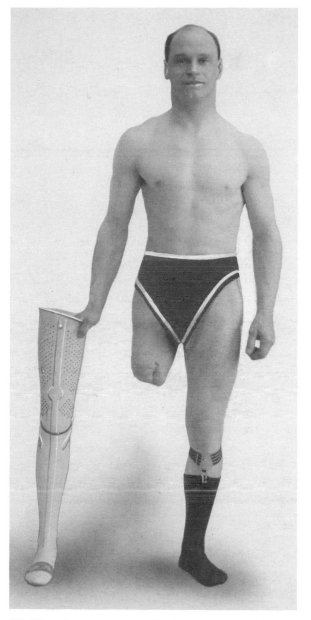

Thus equipped, the company had further useful ammunition in store. When the number of contractors to the Ministry of Pensions was drastically reduced from 14 to two late in 1925, one of the successful contenders was Blatchfords, perhaps because of the 'New Blatchford' leg. Special concessions in the shape of loans were also given to the favoured companies, and the security of this contract ensured the company's stability for the next ten years.

As part of the company's new-found ebullience, and to clear the way for the prototype limb newly sanctioned for trial by the Ministry, Chas. and W.A. negotiated for the rights on a metal limb patent which had been granted to Nehemiah Kenney in 1921 and assigned to W.J. Wilson (an Ernst trainee) three years later. An indenture dated 19 February 1925 granted Blatchfords sole and exclusive licence to 'make, use, exercise and vend' the Kenney limb. In exchange for £70, Wilson guaranteed not to make it available to the Ministry or other companies, save only to private patients and trade customers generally. Claimed to weigh 4.5lbs the 'Premier' leg, with weight-adjustable hygienic stump socket and 'patent' ball-bearings throughout, was a useful addition to the Blatchford armoury.

The revolutionary 'New Blatchford' leg for above-knee amputees, made available to all ranks of disabled men and patented 'in all leading countries in the world', was a blend of private inspiration and crafted artistry on the part of the company. This pioneer method of fitting artificial legs by totally enclosing the stump in a suction socket received its proper accolade in a special article in the *British Medical Journal* of 14 November 1925, by 'A Consulting Orthopaedic Surgeon' (E. Muirhead Little, FRCS). Almost at a stroke it rendered obsolete the cumbersome contrivance of straps or suspenders passing over the shoulder and, in the case of short stumps, the additional belt around the pelvis made of steel, leather or

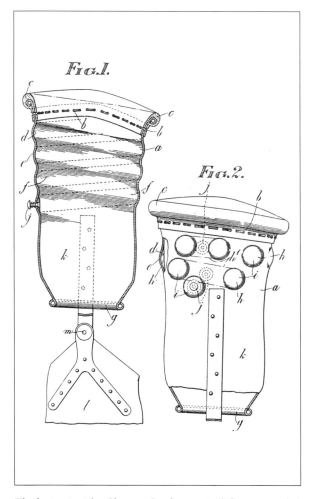

The last patent by Chas., a development of the open-ended socket.

bare stump as closely as possible. Sadly, this was one of the last patent applications made by Chas., since Patent Specification 268,401 of 31 October 1925, for an 'Open-ended socket with projections' received only posthumous acceptance, but like the 'Resiliently held socket-suction' (Patent Specification 269,606) it might be regarded among his finest productions. Both embody his fund of imaginative detail and his intolerance of discomfort to the wearer, in that the finished socket was made of duralumin and the fit was so close that a partial vacuum was created, and a spring valve, fitted to the socket, allowed air in when the limb was to be detached. The close contact made by the metal socket and the spiral groove held the limb tight, and the absence of friction eliminated sores and permitted healthy muscle growth thus increasing the circumference of the stump.

Naturally there was resentment among those now excluded from the Ministry contract. Their business had been seriously curtailed, if not actually shut down, and the usual Questions were asked in the Commons. In reply, Major Tryon, the Minister of Pensions, insisted that because of the refusal by manufacturers hitherto under contract to renew their contracts, except on terms which would involve a greatly increased charge on public funds, a committee of inquiry, presided over by Sir Geoffrey Collins, had investigated the position of certain firms deemed to have formed a combination against the government. Thanks to the committee, a cheaper supply of first-rate quality artificial limbs had been secured, and the House would wish him to express the debt of ex-servicemen and of the country generally to the committee. Blatchfords acted energetically, total sales leaping from £33,352 by March 1926 to exceed £39,000 by 1931, when the Ministry's cash advance was repaid.

Willy nilly, old rivals had to find equivalents. M. Masters advertised the life-like nature of

woven fabrics. The prosthesis moved with the stump as though part of it, and the entire absence of body harness made it eminently suitable for women.

Initially the home-made creation of an amputee, Ernest Underwood, a former weight lifter of championship rank injured in the war, Blatchfords began in 1924 to refine his rather crude socket design, turned on a lathe with 3–4-inch annular grooves on the inside fitting the their new metal leg with internal tendon, attached by means of their patented 'Surhold' hip joint and pelvic band, enabling shoulder braces to be dispensed with. Grossmith's improved Anglesey legs were unsurpassed for lightness; their foot for the Syme's amputation the neatest and lightest, and their patented 'security' attachment also dispensed with shoulder straps. But Blatchfords could luxuriate in the contract, and during this calm and well-modulated period, the co-directors' annual income after the death of Chas. rarely fell below £3,250 each, and patents, brochures, offprints and catalogues began to flow.

Chas. lived just long enough to see his company set fair for the foreseeable future. He passed away on 13 April 1926 in his 64th year, at the family home, 90 Clapham Road. A measure of his and his sons' achievement is the size of his estate, quoted in *The Times* of 8 March 1927 as £22,355, with net personal property as £20,655. Cash in the bank totalled over £11,000 and stocks and shares almost £5,000. His liabilities were a mere £614.8s.7d; primarily income tax under Schedules D and E.

At the first meeting of the Executors and Trustees – Tom, W.A. and Philip Edward Broadley Fooks, a partner in the firm of solicitors Arnold, Fooks, Chadwick – on 29 January 1927, the value of Chas's estate was appraised at £24,270. 11s.10d. gross, and £24,245. 5s. 3d. net. There was, however, a small hurdle still to be overcome, the case of *Blatchford and Others* v. *Blatchford*. Details have not survived the massive purge of all classes of legal records ordered in recent years, but the force and validity of the completed draft of the will was successfully proved by the Trustees in the Principal Probate Registry on 21 February 1927. Suffice it to say that Fooks applied the £100 legacy left to him to act as Executor and prove the will to dependants of Chas. who were not provided for in the will, and the money was left

to Mrs James, otherwise Lambert, otherwise Pierpoint and her son, the family not wishing to intervene.

In the will, dated 15 November 1922, after making various specific and financial bequests, Chas. gave the balance of his residuary estate, free of duty, to the Trustees, directing that generous provision be made for his widow, Mary Catherine, then aged 61. Investments of £5,000 Queensland and £4,000 India stock, made after his death, were retained to provide Mary's allowance until her death, after which they would pass to her sons as residuary legatees.

Six hundred £1 shares, valued at 16s. each (£480), left to William Duncan Campbell, were commuted by mutual consent to a cash payment, topped up to £600 as a reminder of the testator's affection for his brother-in-law. These 600 shares were then added to the remainder of the 5,500 shares previously owned by Chas., valued overall at £4,800, and made over to the brothers in equal parts.

Former colleagues and workmates were remembered, notably his foreman, Horace Read, and Ethel Joselin, a descendant of his sister, a beneficiary to the extent of £500, sufficient then for the outright purchase of a modest house. Family bequests included the unexpired 64 years lease on the house in Brixton already occupied by W.A. on a verbal agreement, and worth £650. Upon the death or second marriage of his mother, Tom was to acquire another property in Wilson Road, Camberwell, valued at £265 but sold very soon afterwards for £450.

Tom and W.A. retained the freehold work-shops erected by and belonging to the company at the rear of 90 Clapham Road, but paid the company £580 for their value. A lease-back arrangement for a term of 21 years was agreed at a nominal rental. The absolute title to the freehold of the property known as 'Richmond Cottage', which backed on to Clapham Road, was also passed from the company to its directors for £725. Freehold of 90 Clapham Road proper, excluding the back portion, was estimated at £1,580.

The momentum of events in 1927 saw 500 shares made over to the wives of Tom and W.A.; 88 Clapham Road was sold by the company to the brothers for £1,000, and under the terms of two agreements, Masters and Sons, in consideration of a sum of £2,000, assigned to Blatchfords benefits of contracts with the Ministry to be held by them as from 1 July 1927, and agreed the underlease of a 'hut' at Roehampton until 25 March 1932, at a rent of £25 a year. Fettes resigned as auditor to become Company Secretary, a post which carried with it an annual fee of £80.

With regard 'to the present circumstances', at a directors meeting on 27 March 1928, it was decided to close the Maintenance Reserve Account by means of transfers of £5,000 to the Reserve Account, £1,625 to the Premises Account, £295 to the account for 88 Clapham Road and £255 to Profit and Loss. Profit for the year was over £7,000, so it was agreed to allot each director £3,250 by way of salary. In June 1932 shareholders were asked to confirm transfer of a further £1,500 from the Appropriation Account to the Reserve Fund, and that £9,000 be written off against the former, a figure standing to the debit of the directors in respect of special expenditure on behalf of the company. In August the company's Seal was affixed to an agreement of the lease of premises at Roehampton, and each director's remuneration set at £4,250.

An interesting sidelight on company prosperity in October 1933 is a document drawn up between Tom, then aged 47 and living in Clapham Park, and his younger brother, not far away in Drewstead Road, Streatham Hill. It notes that the directors had been receiving by way of salary and remuneration for their services a sum equivalent to 60 per cent of the certified net profits of the company, the balance of which was placed in a Reserve or Appropriation Account, then some £8,000. The brothers agreed that on the death of either of them, the survivor would be appointed Chairman and Managing Director and take out a three-year service contract, for which he would receive 40 per cent of the net profits. A new director would be appointed to represent the interests of the deceased, and would receive a sum equal to a further 20 per cent of the net profits, to be paid to the personal representatives of the deceased. The remaining 40 per cent would be carried into the appropriate account. Witnessed by Fettes, this agreement was cancelled by mutual consent in the dog days of September 1935.

How much the directors, their advisers and contacts in the trade knew about the Ministry of Pensions' decision to withhold the contract from Blatchfords in 1935, we shall never know for certain. Nor whether timely provision was made to find other clients. Evidence is contradictory. Sales figures for the three preceding years of £41,516, £42,382 and £42,465, together with static wage bills, may argue a degree of introspective complacency, a management impervious to outside factors. In Liverpool, a tenancy had just been agreed with the Royal Liver Friendly Society for premises, yet at Cardiff a yearly rent reduction had been won in 1933. Advertising expenditure, which had fallen from £597, when the 'New' limb was launched, to just £66 in 1932–3, did rise the next year to £177, so possibly there was advance warning of dire straits. A whole-page display advertisement in the *Medical Directory* for 1936 swallowed up part of the £500 budget for that year, a high level of spending on publicity which was to last until the outbreak of war. Whatever the case may be,

The Ministry of Pensions letter cancelling the contract.

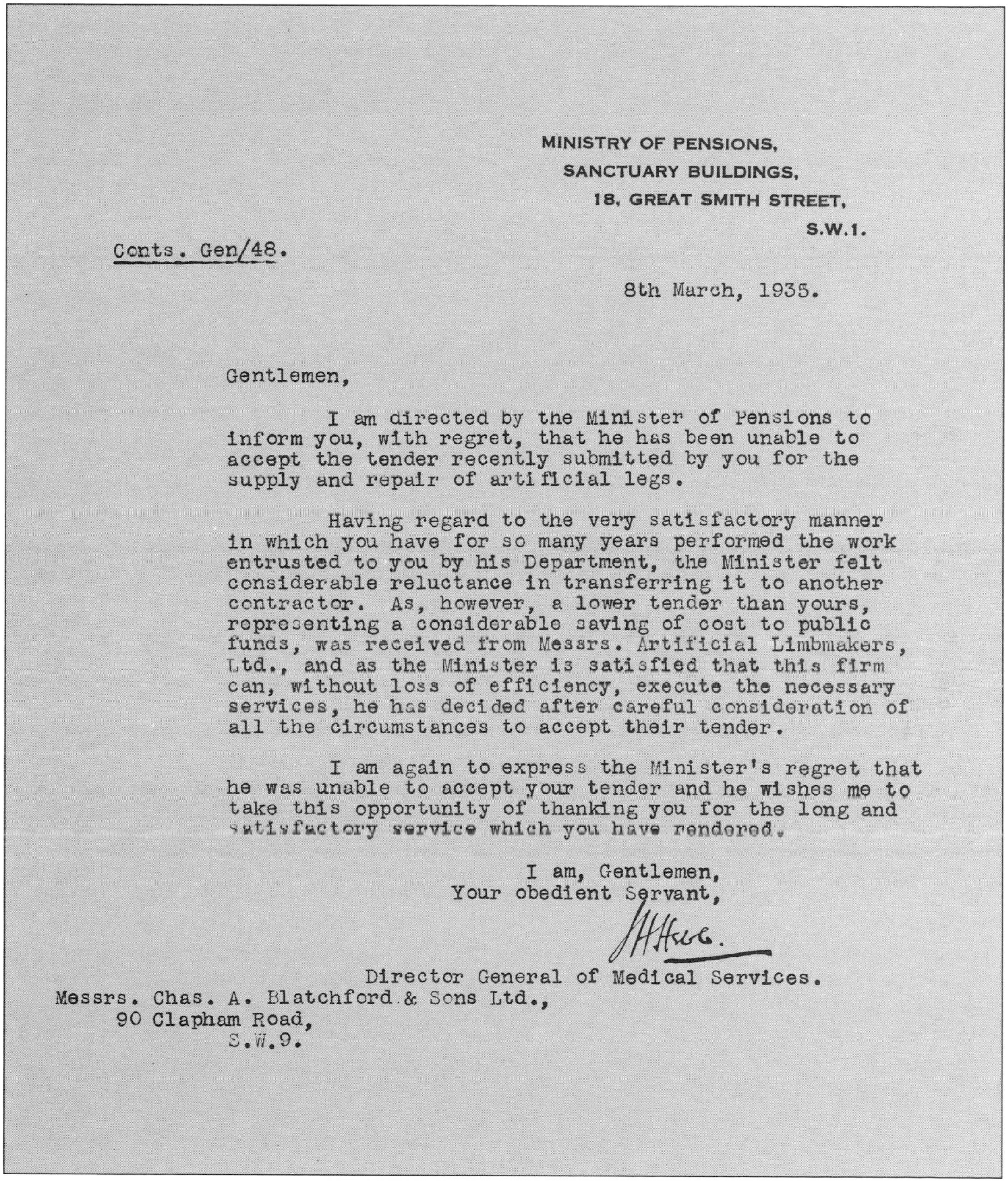

MINISTRY OF PENSIONS,
SANCTUARY BUILDINGS,
18, GREAT SMITH STREET,
S.W.1.

Conts. Gen/48.

8th March, 1935.

Gentlemen,

    I am directed by the Minister of Pensions to inform you, with regret, that he has been unable to accept the tender recently submitted by you for the supply and repair of artificial legs.

    Having regard to the very satisfactory manner in which you have for so many years performed the work entrusted to you by his Department, the Minister felt considerable reluctance in transferring it to another contractor. As, however, a lower tender than yours, representing a considerable saving of cost to public funds, was received from Messrs. Artificial Limbmakers, Ltd., and as the Minister is satisfied that this firm can, without loss of efficiency, execute the necessary services, he has decided after careful consideration of all the circumstances to accept their tender.

    I am again to express the Minister's regret that he was unable to accept your tender and he wishes me to take this opportunity of thanking you for the long and satisfactory service which you have rendered.

        I am, Gentlemen,
      Your obedient Servant,

           Director General of Medical Services.

Messrs. Chas. A. Blatchford & Sons Ltd.,
    90 Clapham Road,
      S.W.9.

BLATCHFORD LIMBS

The Finest in the World

SOLE SUPPLIERS OF THE WONDERFUL LIMB WITHOUT BRACE OR BELT OF ANY KIND.

LIGHT MODERN ARTIFICIAL ARMS AND LEGS FOR ALL AMPUTATIONS **AND ALL SURGICAL APPLIANCES**

The limb illustrated here has been exhaustively studied by eminent orthopædic surgeons and has been fully reported on in the British Medical Journal. Further particulars willingly supplied to any Member of the Medical Profession.

PHONE: RELIANCE 3567.

CHAS. A. BLATCHFORD & SONS, LTD.

90 CLAPHAM ROAD, LONDON, S.W.9

BRANCHES EVERYWHERE

Fully Illustrated Catalogues gladly sent on request

An advertisement from the 1936 Medical Directory.

in 1925 to £14,368 by March 1940, an all-time high having been attained in March 1935, £15,438 just before the loss of contract. Immediately pre-'crash' sales of £42,465, plummeted to £17,041 and for the next few years hovered around the £17,000 mark before world war injuries pushed the numbers upwards. Profits before overheads averaged £19,852 until March 1935, slumping to £7,626 in March 1936 and bottoming out at a record low of £5,505 the following year. The onset of war helped an upward spiral to £7,344, and after three years of net loss, March 1940 saw a return to net profit with £432. Net profits had always been slim: an average of £1,837 for the decade 1925–35, and £143 or so for the next seven years.

Perhaps the most difficult year was 1938–9 which showed a net loss of £316 and directors' salaries were down to £667, another record. Production wages, which had risen from £9,631 in 1925–6 to £12,100 in 1934–5, dropped abruptly, and after the loss of the contract, averaged £7,877 for the financial years 1936–40. Other wages which had been constant around £6,000 slumped to £1,250 during the generally depressed 1930s.

As they began the thankless task of rebuilding, Tom and W.A. were forced into competition with the thrusting, grabbing people of this world. Temperamentally Tom was not one of those prosaic, hard-headed men who see their life's work in terms of market prestige and money; and even with stout support from W.A., it cannot have been easy. A schedule of investments compiled for 1934–6 added up to £6,500, including preferential shares in Harrods, Woolworths, J. Ranks, plus a thousand 4 per cent debenture bonds in the Canadian Pacific Railways, worth £900 in 1934. The family, therefore, had much to lose, quite apart from a natural anxiety for the families of their workers.

'No going back to the 1930s' is a slogan often to be heard nowadays, but most of the people

the seismic shock of this loss of contract on price heralded some lean years, and at this juncture it is worth a brief glance at the company's evolving financial state.

From 1926 to the outbreak of war in 1939, capital stood at £10,000. The Reserve Funds moved from £9,675 in 1926 to £7,500 in 1928–31, peaking at £9,000 in the year ended 31 March 1932. The Profit and Loss figures rose from £358 who utter this slogan have little knowledge of what it was really like and could not even imagine those years. There was little enough money about, wages were very low even if one was in work, and the dole just about kept one alive. The Blatchford workforce of those days are, by their very nature, voiceless, and only a solitary letter exists which touches on staff matters. This, from a Mrs Elsie Jeacocke, was written on 9 December 1937, and thanks W.A. for the tokens of regard for her late husband, William, and for the sum of £194. 7s. 6d. from the Provident Fund.

To drum up financial support, the brothers needed all their father's old will to win. Limb design in the 1930s had stabilised, and there was no miracle Blatchford breakthrough in the offing. No option existed but to sign a contract with Hangers on November 1935. It may have amounted practically to an involuntary renunciation of the firm's birthright but it was sorely necessary. By this agreement Blatchfords (as Licensor) made over to J. E. Hanger of Roehampton House full authority to 'make, use, exercise and sell to the order of the Crown', Blatchfords' sole and exclusive licence for the manufacture and sale of the 'New or Improved Artificial Limb' (Letters Patent No. 249, 269) and received a royalty of £2. 10s. per limb.

When it was claimed that surgical opinion was overwhelmingly in favour of light metal limbs, a Commons spokesman in March 1927 pointed out that the wooden limb had been so far improved that it was actually lighter than the other, and could be more suitable for certain cases of below-knee amputations. More complaints had been received from pensioners wearing metal limbs, and many wished to exchange. Limbs for above-knee amputations made of wood were as light as the prototypes in duralumin. No lighter limb existed than the British Anglesey type, constructed in willow wood, only a small portion of the knee and

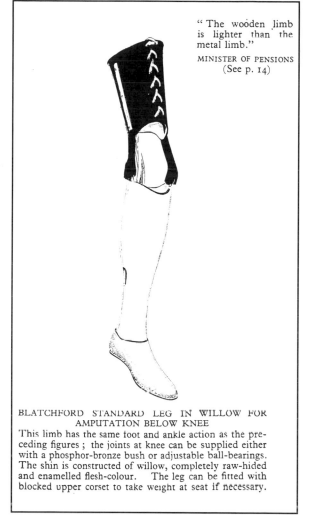

" The wooden limb is lighter than the metal limb."
MINISTER OF PENSIONS
(See p. 14)

BLATCHFORD STANDARD LEG IN WILLOW FOR AMPUTATION BELOW KNEE
This limb has the same foot and ankle action as the preceding figures ; the joints at knee can be supplied either with a phosphor-bronze bush or adjustable ball-bearings. The shin is constructed of willow, completely raw-hided and enamelled flesh-colour. The leg can be fitted with blocked upper corset to take weight at seat if necessary.

The Blatchford standard leg in willow for amputation below the knee.

ankle bolt being of metal. Improved versions of both the Anglesey and Clapper legs were part of the Blatchford repertoire, but in cases where a harness was necessary the Blatchford Standard Leg in willow was as good as any, if not better, and lived up to Chas's proud boast that they were not merely designed to fill the space

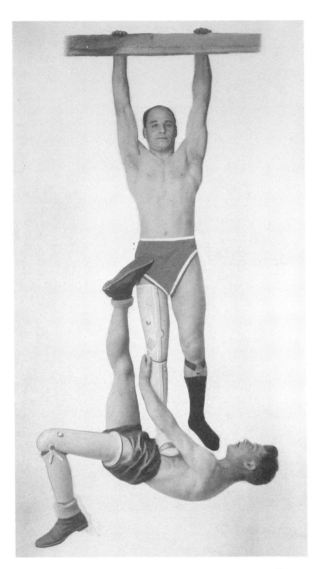

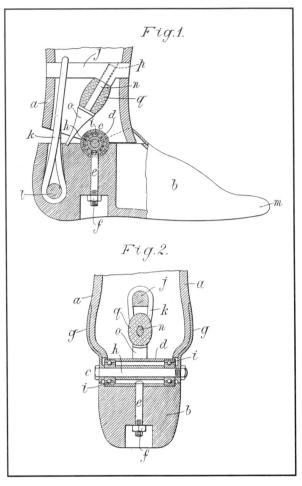

LEFT: The strength of adhesion of the suction socket.

ABOVE: Tendon ankle patented by Blatchfords, 1921.

occupied by the lost natural limb, but actually to take its place as a strong, sensitive and unostentatious member. Both knee and ankle joints had no mortice joints, and no fewer than 96 per cent of the willow limbs supplied to the Ministry of Pensions for ex-servicemen were of this type, and Blatchfords were the sole contractors. Patent Specification 158,410 for a tendon ankle, accepted on 10 February 1921,

indicates the longstanding bias of the brothers' quest for stability linked to lightness.

The experimental workshop set up at Thames Ditton by the Ministry of Supply in 1919, and transferred to Roehampton until closure in 1924, produced only one type of leg, the 'birdcage', so called because it comprised strips of metal, but it did serve as a stimulus to other makers to develop the earliest light-metal limbs. The first consignment of these limbs provided by the Ministry was available for distribution in December 1920. Suppliers at Roehampton offered over 12 makes of artificial limbs, which had on the whole proved successful for different types of amputation, and the Ministry's experts denied comment in the media that they were 'rather an impediment than a help'. As an editorial in the *British Medical Journal* of 18 December 1920 drily remarked: 'It is not, perhaps, to be expected that an article for personal use supplied by a Government department will be accepted... universally without grumbling', so a disproportionate and vocal minority, dissatisfied with their limbs, made public their grievances. Nevertheless, duralumin limbs for below-knee amputation had their supporters, especially within the industry, and for 'lady patients, several of whom are delicate, the change from the old limb to the duralumin limb has been of the greatest benefit' (F.G.Ernst, Branch of Associated Surgical Appliances Makers Ltd, letter to the *British Medical Journal*, 15 January 1921). E. R. Desoutter also chimed in, claiming that light metal limbs could fit long stumps perfectly adequately 'and still make the artificial limb perfectly symmetrical with its fellow, leaving the artificial limb no heavier than would be the case with a shorter stump' (*The Lancet*, 4 December 1926).

The Desoutter leg was held in high regard, and rightly so. Although it was expensive and Desoutter's capacity for output very small, its admirers believed that every person had a right to it. The Ministry, however, was properly reluctant to place itself in the hands of any one firm, and conscious that other light limbs were being tried, they would have faced insuperable difficulty in winning over the Treasury to pay nearly £100 for each of a large number of legs. In fact, for the first issue of 500, the total cost per limb fell below £30. Generally the cost of a leg

for above-knee amputations varied between £15. 10s. and £25, but was still beyond the purses of most hospital Samaritan funds and other charities.

The General Committee of Inquiry on Artificial Limbs, which included Major M. P. Leahy, a Blatchford patient of some distinction, urged that the Desoutter and/or other approved light-metal limbs be placed on the Consolidated List for new cases recommended on surgical or other grounds instead of the standard pattern wooden legs. Because of their undoubted advantages in simplicity and weight – said to be 3.75lbs for above-knee amputations – by 1927 they had gradually ousted the Anglesey among limb wearers.

At about the same time as the Desoutter limb was developed, the J. E. Hanger Company also produced a light-metal limb. As the recognised contractors to the Ministry for the whole of the country, Hangers in 1935 were the main suppliers of all legs at Roehampton, and had 16 branches attached to Ministry of Pensions centres in England, Scotland, Wales, Northern Ireland and Eire. No type of amputation existed which they could not fit satisfactorily and, with a growing export market, they could enjoy a record number of 100,000 satisfied wearers. For upper-limb prostheses, for Hangers read Steepers. Under the banner heading, 'Victory over Empty Sleeves' (1926), Hugh Steeper Ltd concentrated the mind wonderfully on their artificial arms, hands and appliances. As originators and developers of 'the rotary movement at wrist', 'the lateral movement elbow' and 'the truly automatic elbow lock', this company became unchallenged market leaders.

The Blatchford view on the subject, as expressed in a 1920s brochure, was firm, sane and balanced. Metal limbs were billed by many people, new to the industry and whose claims to efficiency were extravagant, as a cure for all possible ills, but the selection of any one

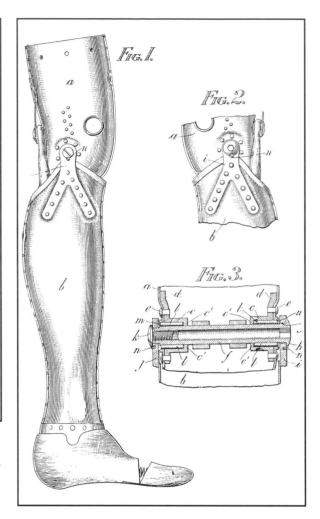

ABOVE: Frank E. Terry's testimonial to regained mobility.

RIGHT: The 1925 metal leg roller-bearing knee, another Blatchford patent.

material did not spell salvation. All 7,000 Blatchford metal limbs, made to the Ministry's format and prints since 1920, were in-house productions from the original conception to the detailed design and manufacture of each part. They were produced to gauged limits with an exactitude unknown to the industry, every part interchangeable. Any lightening of the limb at the expense of durability was seen as incorrect and weight saved by sacrificing proper balance and control of the limb was wrong, as was the provision of insufficient bearing surfaces. This is neatly shown in the roller-bearing knee for a metal leg (Patent Specification 228,284 of 5 February 1925). As distinct from constructions in which the anti-friction members are anchored in self-contained bearings or in cages, here the locking-in position of devices which pivotally connect limb members one to another was ensured. The base of the shin and artificial shin-bone in the Blatchford metal limb was forged and machined from the solid, and even the ankle-bolt – the frictional bearing for the joint – was an integral part of the base. To the best of

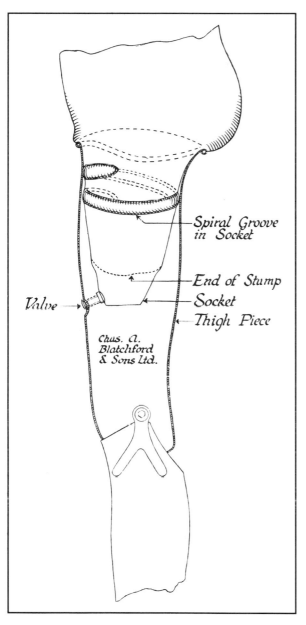

LEFT: Artificial leg without harness, a precursor to the modern-day suction socket.

ABOVE: Major M. P. Leahy boxing with Don McCorkindale.

the constructor's knowledge, it was the only limb made without loose pieces of sheet metal and rivets liable to become detached. The knee-bearing surfaces were identical to those used in the willow leg. The forward motion of the thigh on the shin was arrested by a sophisticated blend of check cord, wheel and spindle, so that by a simple screw adjustment the set of the thigh was self-operated. The Ministry of Pensions accepted 'this limb as one of the best that was ever submitted to it', in sharp contradiction to the unhappy decision of 1935, which brought in its wake Tom's untimely death on 31 July 1938, leaving W.A. to soldier on, the company's sole prop and mainstay. Daisy

Long-distance walkers stride towards the finishing tape.

Blatchford, W.A.'s wife, joined the Board in May 1939, along with the capable Albert Fettes, whose knowledge of the company was exhaustive. Both received 500 of his shares.

With its emphasis on sporting activity, the Desoutter Brothers booklet *Back to Activity* was a tonic for those stunned by the loss of a limb. Marcel Desoutter's advertisements, highlighting his pre-injury love of skiing and riding, mirrored a fierce desire to prove to the world that an artificial limb was no major disability. Sport as a stimulant to self-esteem figured largely in public relations exercises. At club level, cycling, golfing and cricket posed few problems, and an observer from *The Motor* having viewed an Austin Seven circle the Brooklands track at a winning speed of 55.71 m.p.h., was convinced that any legislation concerning disabled drivers was uncalled for and unnecessary. Major Leahy squared up to Don McCorkindale, British heavyweight boxing champion, and in a series of special walking events at athletics meetings, wearers of Blatchford below-knee prostheses broke records for the mile at Herne Hill in 9 minutes 16 seconds, and at Roehampton, the ten-mile mark in 1.45.1. The long-distance walking champions wore the 'New Blatchford' leg, the modern adaptation of knee-stop and control, which embodied cords connected to the braces passed over pulleys which formed an integral part of the base. The stop was fixed at two points, the lower end in the back of the shin and the upper end anchored by the knee-bolt. Widely known as the 'Central Knee Control' (CKC), so lifelike was the effect that a local newspaper noted of the walking contests in 1926 that 'It is practically impossible to tell the walk of a "New Blatchford" wearer and a normal person.' Not all the patents granted were as intricately planned as the CKC innovation for a controlled knee in Patent Specification 132,922 (2 October 1919), which comprised a combination of lower limb pivoted to the upper by a transverse tube, horizontal rigid suspension member and upwardly extending rigid arm, so that the two parts co-operated to clasp tightly; or the later safety knee lock (Patent Specification 158, 096 of 31 January 1921), in which articulated artificial legs locked by pressure, without materially adding to the weight of the limb. Some were rather more mundane inventions to counter leather deterioration, warmth and dampness of the stump, or shaped sockets treated with a wet paste of glue additive incorporated with one or more layers of muslin.

Nothing was too trivial if it affected patient

OPPOSITE: The 1921 safety knee brake.

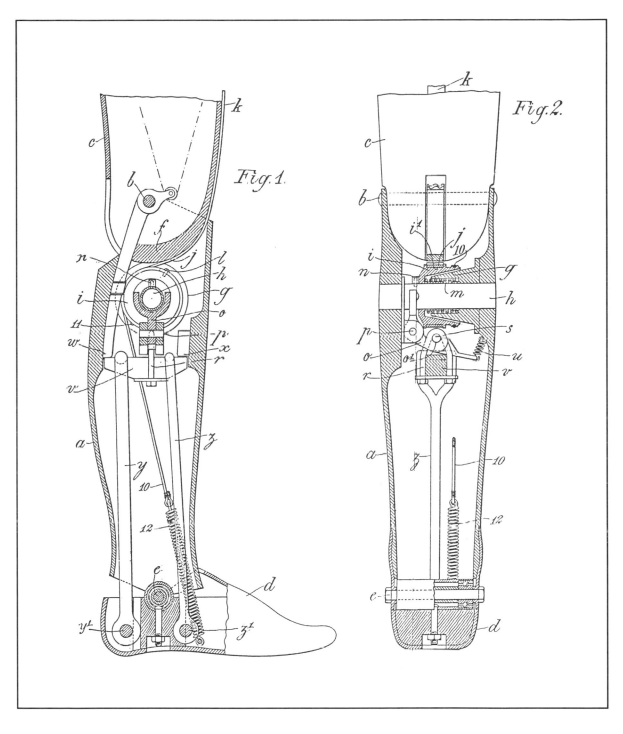

Fig.1.

Fig.2.

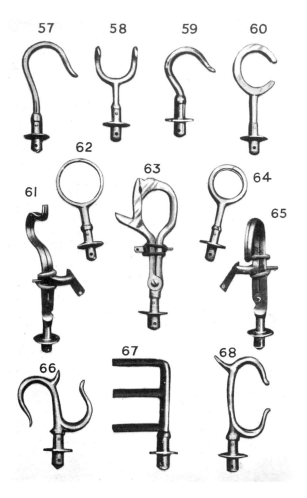

A few hand gadgets produced by Blatchfords for interchangeable adaption to artificial arms.

introduce a 'Velverised' flock finish for use on all Blatchford limbs, especially those with women in mind. Although now less prominently displayed, a selection of arms in common use and suitable for everyday conditions were always available, together with dozens of accessories.

A Memorandum of Agreement between Blatchfords and Peter H. Dorrington to act as sole agent for the goods of the whole company for a period of two years from 1 January 1939, 'over the whole Continent of South America' provides an intriguing list of prices:

'New Blatchford' metal leg (suction socket secure type) ... £30–£35
Hip amputation (willow) ... £22 10s. – £27 10s.
A-K leg (willow) ... £15–£20
T-K leg (willow) ... £15–£20
B-K leg (willow) ... £14–£18
Leg for Symes amputation ... £12–£16
Hip amputation (metal) ... £25–£32 10s.
A-K (metal) ... £18 10s.–£25
B-K (metal) ... £17 10s.–£22 10s.
Pelvic band and hip joint ... £2 10s. 6d. extra
Knee lock ... £1 17s. 6d. extra
Above elbow arm, according to fittings and attachments required ... £16 upwards
Below elbow arm, as above, from £12.

appearance and care; limb makers sought to find ever more efficient means of lubrication to eliminate scraping, squeaking or other noises which could focus unwanted attention on people who preferred not to stand out in a crowd. The special aesthetic needs of women were never overlooked, although it was not until the early 1950s that the firm was able to

How much Dorrington spent of his six-month £50 allowance will never be known. Soon afterwards the pocket-battleship *Graf Spee* was scuttled inside his domain, and Blatchfords went to war again.

CHAPTER SIX

The Second World War

A Martian might be taken aback by the energy with which we knock limbs off and the tenderness with which we replace them.
(*The Lancet*, 13 May 1944)

Force-fed on alarmist media propaganda since the Spanish Civil War of 1936, the staff at Blatchfords would have been almost inhuman not to have shared some part of Stanley Baldwin's belief that 'the bomber must always get through', but in their special case, natural misapprehension was probably tempered by the knowledge, bitter as it was, that after years of enforced low-level output, low-level bombing offered a prescription for commercial recovery.

Thus, mixed feelings prevailed when in June 1938 W.A. joined his fellow limb manufacturers to discuss with the Ministry of Pensions how provision could be made for the estimated high number of air-raid victims requiring urgent treatment. The first assessment since 1863 of hospitals and other buildings ear-marked as auxiliary hospitals had rather fancifully reckoned on over 550,000 bed casualties in the first few months of the war, and the experience and knowledge of the Ministry's Limb Fitting Service, modelled on Roehampton and networked throughout the country, was made ready for the fire over England.

Even so, against a backdrop of evacuation and transfer of patients known as the Emergency Hospital Scheme (EHS), the peace-time annual output of some 5,000 new artificial legs and 500 arms was seen as woefully inadequate. Articulated limbs might have to go by the board in favour of a mass supply of provisional peg legs, made from willow, a wood fortunately obtainable in England and giving the best surgical results. These peg legs would have no knee joints, and for below-knee amputations, a plain joint only, so that even if Roehampton was destroyed, given the necessary materials and labour, production could be stepped up to 25,000 per year, if need be.

Contractual agreements were also reached whereby standards of limb replacement might be lowered and discarded or condemned legs hoarded for emergency use. Moreover, standardised and simplified arms were ready for introduction and an increased supply of Wantage-type crutches provisionally arranged. While the country held its breath, in the not unreasonable expectation of some sort of *blitzkrieg* yet to come, Blatchfords decided on a high profile while its premises remained intact, and lavished £505. 6s.6d. on advertising, while prudently spending £350 on air-raid precautions.

At first, limb makers were able to keep

abreast of the small number of new war cases, chiefly training accidents, and still maintain the supply of new limbs and repair of old ones. This could not last, and even as the number of orders received for artificial limbs rose inexorably from 4,070 in 1939–40 to 6,738 by 1943, enemy air attack and heavy military traffic slowed production and distribution from the factories to the fitting centres. Each of these was a complete unit staffed by medical and technical experts. The year 1944 saw new or enlarged centres emerge right across the country, at Manchester, Cambridge, Reading, Birmingham, Nottingham and Aberdeen. An entirely new centre at Tunbridge Wells eased the burden on Roehampton, where a new limb fitting centre was opened in February 1944, followed by a new wood mill and leather shop housing 85 operatives. Thereafter, as part of those stirring times up to 1948, the Ministry of Pensions Limb Service bore the brunt of limb supply and renewal for upwards of 72,000 new limbs (including duplicates), working not only for British war casualties, past and present, but also for some of the Allies. Roehampton had to expand twice to meet demand, and the permanent brick-built arm factory also expanded in 1943 to double its capacity. The pressure of new war primary arm cases eventually forced the centralisation of new arm supplies and training in their use to Roehampton, Leeds and Glasgow, thus reducing the workload on, for instance, Cardiff, where Blatchfords had in the inter-war years maintained their own representatives.

The long break in Blatchford patent applications, stretching back to 1932, ended with Patent Specification 559,494, applied for on 2 September 1942, the first of a group relating to improvements in artificial arms and elbow joints. In this Patent, W.A. conferred additional sophistication upon the operation of a forearm appliance through the medium of a flexion cord

with improved detachable grip action.

Courses of training in limb-fitting, lectures and demonstrations were organised at and by Roehampton, and wartime experience contributed to the development of national standards of performance, and while a substitute limb is inevitably inferior to the original, art gained upon nature every year. While there were fresh ideas aplenty, the quality of the finished product inevitably began to deteriorate. Shortages of materials for metal artificial legs, such as the substitution of N.A.Alclad 23.S for N.A.Alclad 1780, affected the performance of sockets, and by December 1940, it was impossible to procure 3 per cent nickel steel for forgings. Synthetic rubber, too, replaced the natural product lost to the Japanese forces. The interchange of opinion between the clinical and technical side of the service developed into increasingly close-knit joint ventures in co-ordinated research as the constant flow of innovative concepts from patients, manufacturers and limb surgeons was stimulated by the growing number of casualties. Curiously, controversy still dragged on over the question whether a wood or metal limb for below-knee operations suited the patient better.

Never in history had British life been so relentlessly controlled, and it became the norm to have a bureaucratic form for every type of activity. One such was a circular from the Ministry of Health in November 1942 aimed at Local Education Authorities, pointing out that it was a mistake to delay fitting until children had stopped growing and that it was up to the Authority in the first instance to meet the costs. Parents were then charged an amount not exceeding the cost of treatment, and for renewals and repairs other than stump changes they had to arrange with contractors

Mute evidence of a nation at war: form-filling, circulars and a flow of 'bumpf' from the Ministry.

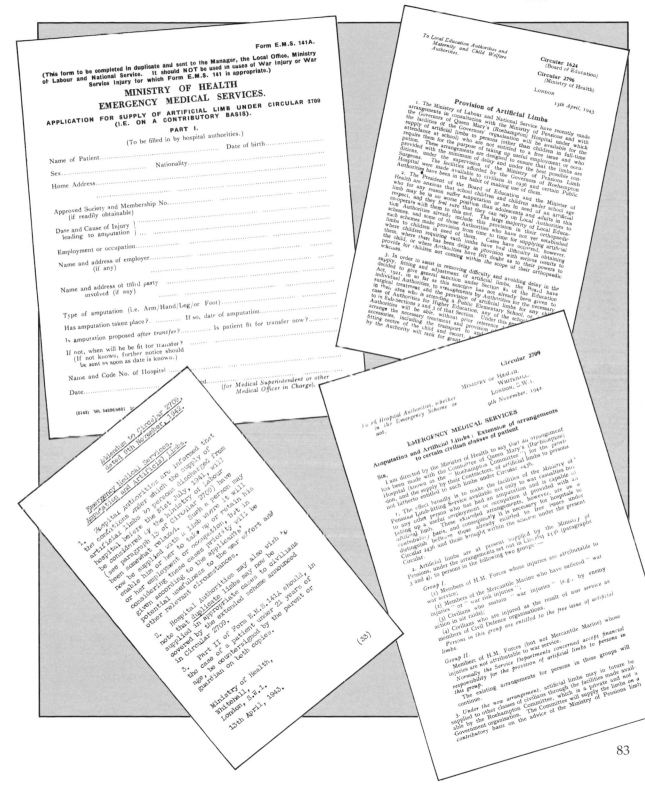

Form E.M.S. 141A.

(This form to be completed in duplicate and sent to the Manager, the Local Office, Ministry of Labour and National Service. It should NOT be used in cases of War Injury or War Service Injury for which Form E.M.S. 141 is appropriate.)

MINISTRY OF HEALTH
EMERGENCY MEDICAL SERVICES.

APPLICATION FOR SUPPLY OF ARTIFICIAL LIMB UNDER CIRCULAR 2709
(I.E. ON A CONTRIBUTORY BASIS).

PART I.

(To be filled in by hospital authorities.)

Name of Patient............................... Date of birth..................

Sex............ Nationality....................

Home Address....................................

Approved Society and Membership No.................
(if readily obtainable)

Date and Cause of Injury }
leading to amputation }........................

Employment or occupation................................

Name and address of employer................................
(if any)

Name and address of third party................................
involved (if any)

Type of amputation (i.e. Arm/Hand/Leg/or Foot).........

Has amputation taken place?........... If so, date of amputation?.........

Is amputation proposed *after transfer*?........... Is patient fit for transfer now?.........

If not, when will he be fit for transfer?
(If not known, further notice should
be sent as soon as date is known.)

Name and Code No. of Hospital.........

Date................................ (for Medical Superintendent or other
Medical Officer in Charge).

(2143) Wt. 34256/4631 10

To Local Education Authorities and
Maternity and Child Welfare
Authorities.

Circular 1624
(Board of Education)
Circular 2796
(Ministry of Health)
LONDON

13th April, 1943.

Provision of Artificial Limbs

1. The Ministry of Labour and National Service have recently made arrangements in consultation with the Ministry of Pensions and with the Governors of Queen Mary's (Roehampton) Hospital and with the facilities of the Governors' organisation for the supply of artificial limbs to persons (other than children in full-time attendance at school) who are not entitled to a free issue and who require them for the purpose of taking up useful employment or occupation. These arrangements are designed to ensure that the limbs are provided with the minimum of delay and under the best possible conditions, under the supervision of the Ministry of Pensions Limb Surgeons. The facilities afforded by the Governors of Roehampton Hospital were made available to civilians in 1936 and certain Public Authorities have been in the habit of making use of them.

2. The President of the Board of Education and the Minister of Health are anxious that school children and children under school age who for any reason suffer amputation or are in need of an artificial limb may be in no worse position than adolescents and adults in this respect, and they feel sure that they can rely on Local Authorities to co-operate with them to this end. The large majority of Local Education Authorities already include this provision in their orthopaedic schemes, and some of those Authorities who have not yet established such schemes make provision from time to time to supplying artificial limbs to children in need of them. Cases have been known, however, where there has been delay and real difficulty in obtaining them, or where Authorities have felt doubt as to their powers to provide for children not coming within the scope of their present schemes.

3. In order to assist in removing difficulty and avoiding delay in the supply, fitting and adjustment of artificial limbs, the Board have decided to give general sanction under Section 80 of the Education Act, 1921, in so far as this sanction has not already been given to individual Authorities, to arrangements by Authorities for the necessary surgical treatment and the provision of artificial limbs for any child in their area who is attending a Public Elementary School, or, in the case of Authorities for Higher Education, any of the children referred to in Sub-Sections 2 and 3 of that Section. Under this sanction the Authorities will be able, without prior sanction in each case, to arrange the necessary treatment and provision and reference to the accessories, including the transport to and from the fitting centre of the child and escort, and the provision by the Authority will rank for grant.

Addendum to Circular 2709,
dated 9th November, 1942.

Emergency Medical Services.
Amputation and Artificial Limbs.

1. Hospital Authorities are informed that the conditions under which persons discharged from hospital before the 31st July, 1944, will be considered in of Circular 2709) have been somewhat relaxed. Such a person may now be supplied with a limb where it will enable him or her to take up or retain his or her employment or occupation, but in considering these cases priority will be given according to the applicants' potential usefulness to the war effort and other relevant circumstances.

2. Hospital Authorities may also wish to note that duplicate limbs may now be supplied in appropriate cases to civilians covered by the extended scheme announced in Circular 2709.

3. Part II of Form E.M.S.141A should, in the case of a patient under 21 years of age, be countersigned by the parent or guardian on both copies.

Ministry of Health,
Whitehall,
London, S.W.1.
13th April, 1943.

(33)

Circular 2709

MINISTRY OF HEALTH,
WHITEHALL,
LONDON, S.W.1.
9th November, 1942.

To all Hospital Authorities, whether
in the Emergency Scheme or
not.

EMERGENCY MEDICAL SERVICES

Amputation and Artificial Limbs: Extension of arrangements
to certain civilian classes of patient

SIR,

I am directed by the Minister of Health to say that an arrangement has been made with the Committee of Queen Mary's (Roehampton) Hospital (known as the Roehampton Committee") for the provision, and the supply by their Contractors, of artificial limbs to persons not hitherto entitled to such limbs under Circular 2436.

1. The effect broadly is to make the facilities of the Ministry of Pensions Limb-fitting Service available not only to war casualties but to any other person who has had an amputation if provided with an artificial limb, it is necessary for hospitals to take up a useful employment or occupation, however, under a contributory basis, and consequently it is necessary for hospitals to distinguish between those already entitled to free issues under Circular 2436 and those brought within the scheme under the present Circular.

2. Artificial limbs are at present supplied by the Ministry of Pensions, under the arrangements set out in Circular 2436 (paragraphs 3 and 4), to persons in the following two groups:—

Group I.
(1) Members of H.M. Forces whose injuries are attributable to war service;
(2) Members of the Mercantile Marine who have suffered "war injuries" or "war risk injuries" (e.g. by enemy action in air raids);
(3) Civilians who sustain "war injuries" as the result of war service as members of Civil Defence organisations.
(4) Civilians who are injured as the result of the free issue of artificial limbs.
Persons in this group are entitled to the free issue of artificial limbs.

Group II.
Members of H.M. Forces (but not Mercantile Marine) whose injuries are not attributable to war service.
Normally the Service Departments concerned accept financial responsibility for the provision of artificial limbs to persons in this group.
The existing arrangements for persons in these groups will continue.

3. Under the new arrangement, artificial limbs may in future be supplied to other classes of civilians through the facilities made available by the Roehampton Committee, which will supply the limbs on a Government organisation. The Committee will supply the limbs on a contributory basis on the advice of the Ministry of Pensions limb

83

accordingly. Mechanically and surgically approved standard-issue legs cost £13–£19 for wooden ones and £22–£32 for metal (both excluding exceptional types). Arms varied between £12. 10s. and £30.

The Second World War, like its predecessor, acted as a solvent for social change and within a year or so the EHS lost the original target of civilian war casualties and the needs of the Forces, and it became more like a national hospital service. Outside the hospitals, though, little had changed. The National Health Insurance scheme was still limited to general practitioner treatment, and although the income limit for insured persons was raised from £250

Blatchfords at Roehampton in 1942: a toe-hold at the front gate.

to £420 at the beginning of 1942, dependants were still excluded. Civilian air-raid victims in 1940 were given one limb free of charge, duplicates being added by March 1943. Schoolchildren who lost limbs other than by enemy action, however, were not entitled to the free issue and were fitted on a contributory basis under the aegis of the Ministry of Health.

A House of Lords case in 1942, *Steele* v. *George Robert & Co.*, showed the regrettable gap which industry and the law tolerated between compensation and rehabilitation for further employment. The supply of artificial limbs was not a compulsory part of benefit under the Workmen's Compensation Act, and Herbert Morrison promised it would be part of a government package to be introduced as soon as possible after the end of the war. Meanwhile, as

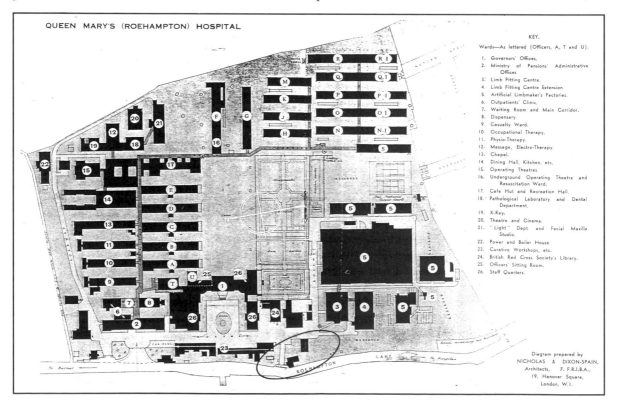

QUEEN MARY'S (ROEHAMPTON) HOSPITAL

KEY.

Wards—As lettered (Officers, A, T and U).

1. Governors' Offices.
2. Ministry of Pensions' Administrative Offices.
3. Limb Fitting Centre.
4. Limb Fitting Centre Extension.
5. Artificial Limbmaker's Factories.
6. Outpatients' Clinic.
7. Waiting Room and Main Corridor.
8. Dispensary.
9. Casualty Ward.
10. Occupational Therapy.
11. Physio-Therapy.
12. Massage, Electro-Therapy.
13. Chapel.
14. Dining Hall, Kitchen, etc.
15. Operating Theatres.
16. Underground Operating Theatre and Resuscitation Ward.
17. Cafe Hut and Recreation Hall.
18. Pathological Laboratory and Dental Department.
19. X-Ray.
20. Theatre and Cinema.
21. "Light" Dept. and Facial Maxilla Studio.
22. Power and Boiler House.
23. Curative Workshops, etc.
24. British Red Cross Society's Library.
25. Officers' Sitting Room.
26. Staff Quarters.

Diagram prepared by
NICHOLAS & DIXON-SPAIN,
Architects, F. F.R.I.B.A.,
19, Hanover Square,
London, W.1.

part of emergency schemes for rehabilitation of injured workpeople, additional facilities would be provided for limb fitting. These schemes, including vocational guidance courses, were initiated by the Ministry of Labour to provide limbs on a repayment basis for males aged 14–65, as an incentive to return to work, and they increased the demand made upon the limb manufacturers. Females up to the age of 60 were similarly co-opted, and those not already busy with war work had to be certified as capable, if supplied with an artificial limb, of carrying on their duties as housewives.

In 1943, a new and slightly amended contract was agreed between the Ministry and its leg contractors, the existing contract having expired. Two years later, in commenting on the White Paper, 'Artificial Limbs', published by the Ministry of Pensions in 1945, the *British Medical Journal* wondered whether it was right to eliminate competition by placing the contract for the manufacture and supply of limbs with any one firm. Under the guidance of W.A., Blatchford limbs were again being supplied to

the Ministry, albeit not on a major scale. Fittingly, W.A.'s salary at this date was on a par with that of a hospital consultant, although the differential in favour of the latter widened considerably when new pay scales for medical men came into effect in 1948.

Despite the growth in the number of people engaged in the trade, the time lag in the completion of orders caused great concern. Sir Walter Womersley, Minister of Pensions, quoted in *Hansard* (March 1944), said that he was having discussions with contractors 'who are making serious efforts to improve the position'. More skilled workers were to come on stream, though where they were to come from was left unanswered. Even assuming the miraculous advent of trained craftsmen overnight, the company was just about to take out a £5,000-limit overdraft, money was tight, and head office could never have physically housed them. Its allotment of space at Roehampton was hardly palatial and impatient claims by limb makers to requisition larger premises would have been seen in a very dim light at the time.

April 1945 – March 1946

	Clapham Road (total)	Glasgow (total)	Newcastle (total)	Liverpool (total)	Nottingham (total)	Cardiff
Private limbs	1448	1230	2069	1487	2435	3368
- surgical	208					
- repairs	1635					
- sundries	146					
Society limbs	1458					
Trade limbs	6825					
- surgical	12					
- repairs	1226					
- sundries	588					
	13,546					

Total Company output, exclusive of Ministry of Pensions/Roehampton supplies (for which no complete figures are available)   24,135

Causes of single leg amputations and age-incidence in 1658 patients *(The Lancet,* 17 January 1951)								
Age in years	Trauma	Osteomyelitis	Congenital	Tuberculosis	Cardiovascular	Diabetes	Other diseases	Unknown causes	Total cases
Under 11	12	7	13	2	5	0	6	43	88
11–20	38	15	9	12	12	0	20	33	139
21–30	69	34	4	19	21	0	33	75	255
31–40	127	39	9	28	34	4	42	99	382
41–50	99	41	16	23	66	4	48	6	350
51–60	87	16	1	16	70	15	39	38	282
61–70	34	22	0	7	46	7	16	17	149
Over 70	3	1	0	1	5	0	3	0	13

The Blatchford wages book for 1944–5 lists by name some 66 individuals. Time and distances were concertinad in those days, so that people lived closer to their work, but bearing in mind the arduous circumstances under which they toiled, it is instructive to glance at the wages received by a random sample of the men who, in those frenetic times, achieved so much. Excluding production bonuses, and taking into account sickness absences, in the period October 1943 – September 1944, of the 19 manual workers in the Wood Shop, Messrs Forster, Bray, Shreeve and Mann averaged £5. 2s. a week. Their 21 counterparts in the Metal Shop, exemplified by Messrs Sargeant, McNab, Hutton and Moody, could be reasonably assured of £6. 5s. weekly.

Including supplies of new primary limbs, the average combined wartime output of all health centres, taken over several months, as given in *The Civilian Health and Medical Services*, Vol. 2 (HMSO, 1955) shows:

New legs...982; New arms...182
Repairs to legs...3,269; Repairs to arms...192
Repairs to limbs sent through the post...1,829
Cases handled per month...4,609.

How Blatchfords performed can be gleaned from the table on page 85, one of precious few war era statistics.

Output for the whole firm was therefore 24,135, an average of 2,011 for each month. Of all the branches, the best batting average was 281 jobs at Cardiff, with the smaller staff at Glasgow propping up the rest at 103.

The struggle for a national health service was protracted and was conducted as internecine warfare between the health authorities and the medical profession, both parties seen by many as self-serving, immovable and monolithic objects. A first indication of medical readiness for change came with the Dawson Report of 1921, conceived in post-war euphoria and credited with the outline notion of health centres, including orthopaedic care. Then came the moral authority of the Beveridge Report on a single universal social security scheme. Published in December 1942, during the needle-sharp, blackest days of the war, it captured popular imagination in an almost messianic way. Essential to any workable social security system was a national health service for all, with paid rehabilitation and industrial training for those who needed it. Despite the impetus to the creation of the national health service instilled by Beveridge, any discussion among the bewildering variety of agencies, official and unofficial, which had sprung up over the previous two decades, had a slightly unreal air until the Labour Party's sweeping victory in the July 1945 General Election. Aneurin Bevan's Cabinet Paper of 5 October 1945, was visionary and comprehensive in scope, offering health and allied services to everyone through central government funding, and not just to the beneficiaries of insurance schemes. After the National Health Service Act of 1946, money no longer stood in the way of advice, early diagnosis and speedy attention became paramount and hospitals were taken into public ownership. Once the medical profession had been weaned from its bout of histrionics and intransigent attitude to any invasion of professional freedoms, the 'Appointed Day' proved to be 5 July 1948, after which the commercial element in medicine was lessened and the National Health Service became not so much a politically inspired state service as 'our own service' (*The Lancet*, 3 July 1948).

The country was still climbing shakily on to its feet after the terrible mauling of the war, but a fully fledged and operational limb service had emerged relatively unscathed. Despite over 200,000 limbs supplied to ex-servicemen, amputees from industry and a host of organisations in the preceding 33 years, there was still a big question mark over whether the industry could cope with the foreseen increase in work. A whole new breed of patients – children with congenital deformities and elderly amputees – poured into the limb centres, over 31,000 in two years, many highlighting the clinical problems of defects at birth or of ageing. Eventually they outnumbered the war-wounded. It was noted in *The Lancet* of 17 February 1951, that of 27,967 new legs ordered for NHS cases since 1948, almost 80 per cent were of duralumin metal, four times the total made from wood, with leather an insignificant 0.01 per cent. A table from the same issue gives some idea of the range of ailments brought by the new civilian patients, acceptable problems well known to limb manufacturers but hitherto paid for individually.

Theoretically the service was well qualified to meet the requirements for prostheses and had made the necessary surgical dispositions, but limb fitting trainees were thin on the ground and the training rudimentary. The slow build-up of staff inhibited the ability of the manufacturers to supply limbs, and everyone from this period recalls the lengthy delays. A three-year waiting list has been mentioned, and Vessa is said to have had its origin in the amount of business 'left lying on the shelf' as the hitherto ignored sections of society claimed their due. At grassroots level, though Blatchfords had craftsmen whose capacity was seen to be much greater than estimated, to maintain production at a new level the company had to take on unskilled labour. Uncertain about the length of the induction period, W.A. had to resort to contracting out for certain parts.

The following letter from the Minister of Pensions, Hilary Marquand, crystallises the welfare spirit of the period and conveys a refreshingly non-doctrinaire approach to competition in a climate unblushingly sold on nationalisation and monopoly control.

(Copy)

Ministry of Pensions.
Sanctuary Buildings,
18, Great Smith Street,
LONDON, S.W.I.
(Dated) 13 November, 1948.

LA/GEN/1074/2

My dear Hughes,

I am writing in reply to your letter of the 18th October…about the supply of artificial limbs under the National Health Service.

As you will know, my Department is acting on behalf of the Ministry of Health…and has, therefore, been responsible for the Limb Service from the 5th July, last.

The supply arrangements were outlined by Buchanan in the House on the 1st July and were debated again on the 22nd July, when my Parliamentary Secretary made it quite clear that we were anxious for the private limb manufacturers to continue in business and to participate in the Scheme.

The arrangements are that any person requiring an artificial limb is asked to attend at the nearest Ministry of Pensions Limb Fitting Centre to his home, there he is examined by a qualified and experienced surgeon who prescribes the type, not make, of limb suitable for the particular stump.

The patient is then given all necessary information to enable him to make an unfettered choice of limb from lists of makers who have entered into a contract for this purpose. If a limb is chosen such as is now being supplied to the war disabled, the patient will get this free of charge. If, however, a limb of some other make is desired and this costs more, the patient will be charged the excess. In this connection, however, we have decided that where the selected limb costs up to £3 more than the one supplied to war disabled pensioners, the additional charge will be met by the Department and not passed on to the patient.

Our chief concern has been to ensure that National Health Service patients get the best possible artificial limbs and there are available for them high quality limbs internationally recognised as among the best in the world, similar to those supplied to the war disabled. It is appreciated that the limbs provided by our own contractors are produced more cheaply because of the very much greater output of the firms concerned and although there would obviously be no justification for paying the excess price from State funds, it was to enable other firms to continue in business that we undertook to pay an additional £3 over the prices of our own contractors.

It is significant that nearly all of the private manufacturers concerned have either entered into a contract with my Department or indicated their desire to do so. Messrs. Desoutter Brothers were, of course, given the opportunity to participate but apparently do not intend taking advantage of it.

The requirement that National Health Service patients should be seen by the experienced limb surgeon of my Department for the purpose of prescribing the particular type of limb and for ensuring that the completed limb is satisfactory in all respects, has been insisted upon for the benefit of the patient. This Limb Surgeon Service is unique and has been built up over the last 30 years or so, and it is right that the benefit of the accumulated experience and expert advice hitherto available to the war disabled should be at the disposal of National Health Service patients. I am quite satisfied therefore that short of paying in full the high prices which might be charged by any particular firm of limb makers, we have done everything possible to enable all manufacturers to continue in business. It is evident from the discussions which have taken place with the Trade that the majority of the firms concerned do not dissent from this view.

While I am sorry that Messrs. Desoutter Brothers are not already within the Scheme I must point out that their decision not to participate cannot be related to restrictions my Department is said to have imposed.

As I have mentioned earlier, our concern is to ensure that patients have the opportunity of being supplied with the best possible artificial limbs. Improvements and new designs, whether they emanate from limb wearers or manufacturers, are carefully investigated by my Research Unit at Roehampton and any improvement is introduced immediately it has the approval of the Standing Advisory Committee which advises me upon matters of this nature. Such improvements will be made available to all limb makers under contract with the Ministry.

It is quite wrong, therefore, to suggest that my Department wishes to create a monopoly or stands in the way of development of improvements in the design and manufacture of artificial limbs. On the contrary, we desire that, subject only to the choice of the patient all our contractors will be able to go on supplying their own make of limb. Some orders have already gone to a number of these firms, many of whom are supplying at prices which enable their limbs to be available as a free issue...

Yours sincerely,

(signed) Hilary Marquand.

Despite, or perhaps as a result of this clear proclamation of government policy, W.A. felt ambivalent at first about the advantages to be gained from contracting into the NHS, and as late as May 1949 wrote 'I am still very uncertain that it is a good business proposition from my point of view'. Earlier, in the depths of the winter of 1948, he and his auditor had made the pilgrimage to Norcross, Blackpool, for an interview with the Director of Contracts and Supplies at the Ministry of Pensions. In the course of this a doubling in the output of Blatchford legs was requested. A revealing exchange of letters ensued, illuminating the fraught situation faced by limb contractors dealing with official diktat in what W.A. described as 'these unusual days of high taxation and political uncertainty'.

Costs

Year to...	Production Wages	Other Wages	Total Sales	Trading Profit	Net Profit
31.3.40	8,235	1,212	19,340	7,344	432
31.3.41	8,557	1,411	20,154	6,904	734
31.3.42	8,937	1,514	19,398	7,078	244
31.3.43	10,302	1,897	22,333	6,795	178
31.3.44	13,126	2,255	26,535	7,524	293
8 months to...					
30.11.44	11,616	1,603	22,965	6,630	1,601
Year to...					
30.11.45	12,249	2,548	28,630	9,056	1,183
30.11.46	12,323	2,522	28,005	9,312	1,249
30.11.47	12,864	2,730	28,774	9,175	991
30.11.48	10,014	7,053	27,450	10,419	(1,252)
30.11.49	17,739	10,051	43,080	17,066	(183)
30.11.50	26,708	10,880	65,352	21,635	2,010

W.A. anticipated that with a re-organisation of office and stores layout, and granted more labour and enhanced production methods, it would be possible to increase output to 50 limbs per week by June 1949. In a letter dated 3 January 1949, he pointed out that whereas provision had been made to protect the Ministry should costs fall, no such protection was accorded the contractor, and the prices agreed under the present contract had been hurried through and imperfectly costed.

A reasonably guaranteed market for Blatchfords' output was essential if he was to find additional working capital of £10,000, plus the cost of buying new factory space if rented premises could not be found. W.A. was 'not unappreciative of your suggestion that my existing contract might be extended a further three to five years' but the likelihood of further wage increases might neutralise this benefit. The Ministry's reply, a week later, reiterated the freedom of choice allowed to patients which meant that a guaranteed market was just not possible. Quality of workmanship determined choice, and the number of orders already received by the firm, coupled with those diverted from J.E. Hanger, to spread production more evenly, should enable Blatchfords to compete with others 'whose limbs may not be of such a high standard'. With no sign of a downward trend in demand, already in excess of the total productive capacity of the industry, it was agreed that it was unreasonable to expect Blatchfords to incur capital expenditure on a short-term contract due to expire in July 1950.

An extended contract incorporating a wage variation clause would be placed on the table, provided W.A. could undertake 3,000 legs a year. Still in January 1949, W. A. riposted with an offer of 2,500 legs, provided the contract was extended to July 1955 and contained the clause on wages, when any increases were general throughout the trade.

The government took time to learn about the size of capital investment essential to proper funding of developing community services, and in the general gravity of post-war blight could do precious little to help find suitable accommodation for smaller firms or assist with cash for refurbishing and extensions. Acute restriction on building plants meant that many limb fitting agencies had communal rooms foisted upon them, so that Blatchfords were not alone in feeling, if not quite pariahs, then certainly non-priorities.

The branches perhaps suffered more than most. In the quest for bricks and mortar, Birmingham appears to have had the least money to play with. Tenancy, therefore, on the Bordesley premises was terminated from December 1941, when, in W.A.'s words, 'we have tried to keep this branch open, but unfortunately it has run at a loss for quite a long while', this despite a rent reduction offered in June 1938. Under another agreement, dated 2 December 1941, the branch moved to Lower Temple Street, taking two rooms on the second floor at a yearly rental of £100. Notwithstanding a tenancy agreement signed on 9 March 1943, Blatchfords were compelled to quit Dominions House in Cardiff in favour of the Postmaster General. In the search for new premises, full support came from one Ministry, Pensions, but another, Works, proved implacable, resisting W.A.'s best efforts to force its hand: 'In view of the amount of work we are now undertaking in Cardiff, failure to find alternative accommodation would seriously delay the fitting up of the disabled to take their rightful place in industry.' Similar pressing problems were acute in Manchester. Here the company shared rooms in Sunlight House with Ideal Limbs, but there were difficulties over split accommodation where female patients were concerned, and Vokes had their eye, too, on the same fitting room, work room and waiting room in Crown Buildings.

By a happy coincidence, both W.A.'s sons

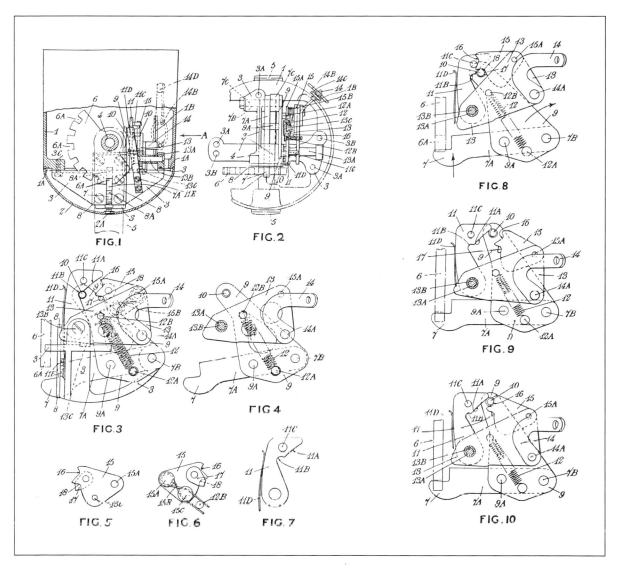

FIG.1 FIG.2 FIG.3 FIG 4 FIG.5 FIG.6 FIG.7 FIG.8 FIG.9 FIG.10

came of age during these momentous episodes in the social upheaval in Britain, serendipity indeed for the company, permitting the first changes in shareholdings since 1927. Such an opportune infusion of youthful zest and fresh thinking can only have heartened W.A., who had himself spent just over 21 years with the company when, in 1940, the executors of Tom's estate allocated 1,000 shares to William Charles

Details from Brian's first Patent Specification (1953): refinements to the elbow joint connecting the upper arm and forearm portions, easier to make and quieter in action.

(Bill). Daisy, W.A.'s wife, was given 500 shares, but the lion's share, 3,000, went to the man who had carried the company through the Depression years and now had little option but

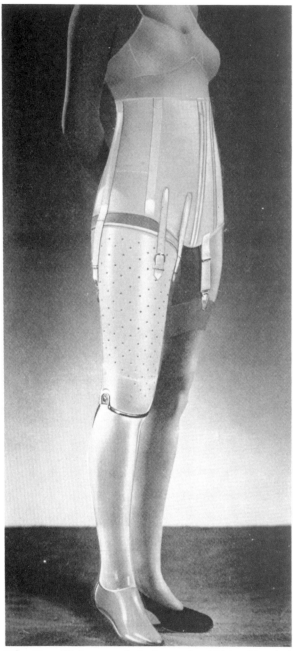

The 'Prosilia' corset belt from the 1940s, blended suspension for the artificial limb with a neat and comfortable foundation garment.

to brace everyone for a new baptism of fire. An undated typescript note confirms W.A.'s obligation to pay Susan Blatchford, Tom's widow, £8,731 10s. for the value of the shares, plus £1,250 for the value of a half-share of the freehold of 90 Clapham Road. By so doing, she relinquished all ties with the company and stepped down from the Board.

In the midst of the debate over the implications of the NHS, Brian Geoffrey attained his majority and W. A. made over to his younger son 1,000 shares, and in the process brought on to the scene a potent and dedicated force for the future. He was not to join the Board as a director until December 1952, but was already deeply wedded to the engineering tradition and would fully live up to the old adage of cometh the hour, cometh the man. Received opinion has it that at the inception of the NHS, by request of the Ministry of Health, Blatchfords' efforts were concentrated on producing legs and the production of arms ceased. Yet the first patent in Brian's name (Patent Specification 750, 371), first applied for in December 1953 and published on 13 June 1956, was for an elbow joint easier to make and maintain than previous versions. With a selector neatly operated from the pull cord, it gave a greater range of arm flexion, was quieter and more reliable in action and gave increased room in the upper arm residue for a stump.

Brian's older sister, Joyce Lilian, received share numbers 5001–6000 at the same time, and in the dispersal among the family of Hugh Steeper Limited's Blatchford shares in 1951, her stake was pushed up to 1,500, Brian's increased by 1,000, Daisy by 500 and Bill by another 500.

As is shown in the table on page 89, net profit and total sales fluctuated throughout the war years. To survive a succession of alarms and excursions off-stage the company still augmented its takings with the sale of products displayed in surgical appliances catalogues. One such, aimed primarily at female customers, listed the 'Herncase' rupture support at 35s. and a wide range of trusses, elastic hosiery, the most popular corsets, brassières, colostomy appliances, maternity, sacroiliac and other surgical belts.

Profits after tax in November 1944 of £1,601 was an improvement on the previous year, but a welcome influx of new money had to be covered by a guarantee given to Hugh Steeper Ltd in February 1945 for £2,500, supported by Stock Exchange securities, to cover their acquisition of a corresponding number of shares in Blatchfords. By January 1951 this guarantee was no longer required, Steepers having ceded their 2,500 shares back to the company to wrap up a lengthy financial imbroglio involving the firm of Ideal Limbs Ltd.

An unsatisfactory state of affairs persisted for many years over monies owed to the company by Ideal Limbs. This company had been incorporated in November 1944 as manufacturers of and dealers in artificial limbs and orthopaedic appliances, as well as the usual array of dental, medical, surgical and optical instruments. Its directors were Frederick Taylor and Albert George Fettes, with W.A. as a shareholder. The sum involved was not inconsiderable and proceedings on the debt were left unresolved until a Board meeting in December 1950 arrived at an equitable solution. As a consequence, W.A. retired from the Board of Ideal Limbs and transferred all his shares in that company to Mr Hugh Steeper, who, with his financial adviser, was present at the meeting. In consideration thereof, Hugh Steeper passed all his Blatchford shares to W.A. or his nominees, together with a sum of £1,500, to be paid on or before 31 December 1952.

Altogether, bearing in mind the number of people under his command at this time, W.A. needed every iota of belief in his workforce if the increased quota of 2,500 legs offered to the Ministry of Pensions was to be fulfilled. But in the end he had his way and the company boasts a copy of a covering letter, signed for the Director of Contracts and Supplies and dated 4 August 1949, giving W. A. his five year contract and bargaining rights on wages – a happy omen for the quieter waters of the 1950s.

CHAPTER SEVEN

Brian, Basingstoke and the BSK

Concessions hard won from the Ministry of Pensions on the annual output of limbs expected of Blatchfords were achieved only through tough bargaining by W.A., and, as the circular sent out soon afterwards hints, few in the company harboured illusions about an idyllic future. Having only a small segment of the market, Blatchfords had to work relentlessly to retain and build upon that share. In anticipation of the NHS contract, the company in 1948 engaged extra staff, and perhaps the first to join the cadre of pre-war and wartime veterans was a small contingent from the 'Rolls-Royce' of the industry, the firm of Desoutters in Hendon.

Between 1947 and 1948 much extension work took place at the Roehampton Limb Fitting Centre and factories, but working in splendid isolation in a hut approximately 40ft x 18ft, under conditions rated by its occupant as pre-industrial revolution, was the sole fitter for Blatchfords at Roehampton, the eloquent and imaginative Herbert 'Tommy' Thompson. For him the 'Picket Hut' is unforgettable; named after the First World War servicemen who absconded without passes to the local pub in Roehampton village, it was the setting for much

calm reflective development work for Blatchfords over the years. The Patella Tendon Bearing (PTB), an entirely new concept in Britain, featuring the first use in limb manufacture of plastics in the form of glass-fibre reinforced polymer resins, was but one of numerous changes which came under intense scrutiny in the 'Hut'.

An accomplished prosthetist, Thompson believes he could fit anything but he would readily agree that it became the province of Brian to adapt and make practical even the most fanciful ideas, flashes of insight, or problems encountered by the prosthetists at the branches. Once briefed, Brian would go to work immediately, sketching on the nearest serviette or whatever else lay within reach. As a designer Brian was incomparable, and from the outset his powerful sense of outrage at the mediocre limbs on offer to amputees in an otherwise enlightened and mature civilisation drove him to a ceaseless programme of research and development. Ideas from all sources were translated into reality, or, if simulation of user conditions in a laboratory situation indicated there was no engineering solution, he, with John Shorter, his assistant from 1966, would try and

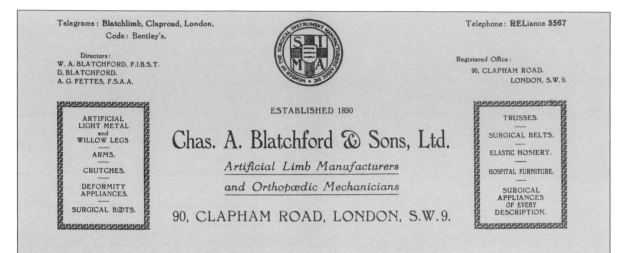

Telegrams: **Blatchlimb, Claproad, London.**
Code: Bentley's.

Telephone: RELiance **3567**

Directors:
W. A. BLATCHFORD, F.I.B.S.T.
D. BLATCHFORD.
A. G. FETTES, F.S.A.A.

Registered Office:
90, CLAPHAM ROAD,
LONDON, S.W.9.

ARTIFICIAL
LIGHT METAL
and
WILLOW LEGS
—
ARMS.
—
CRUTCHES.
—
DEFORMITY
APPLIANCES.
—
SURGICAL BOOTS.

ESTABLISHED 1890

Chas. A. Blatchford & Sons, Ltd.

Artificial Limb Manufacturers

and Orthopædic Mechanicians

90, CLAPHAM ROAD, LONDON, S.W.9.

TRUSSES.
—
SURGICAL BELTS.
—
ELASTIC HOSIERY.
—
HOSPITAL FURNITURE.
—
SURGICAL
APPLIANCES
OF EVERY
DESCRIPTION.

Dear Sir or Madam

We have much pleasure in advising you that we have been officially appointed as Manufacturers and Suppliers of Artificial Limbs under the new National Health Scheme. In these circumstances we would appreciate it if we could continue to supply your requirements in the future as we have done in the past.

When you require repairs or replacements the procedure to be followed is that you apply, preferably by letter, to the Secretary of the Government Limb Fitting Centre nearest to your home.

If, as we sincerely hope, you have been satisfied with our previous service, may we suggest that, in your first ordering under the new scheme, you state that you desire your order to be undertaken by "Blatchford's."

If we can assist you further in any way, please do not hesitate to write us.

Assuring you of our best service and attention at all times.

Yours faithfully,

CHAS. A. BLATCHFORD & SONS, Ltd.

And at Birmingham, Cardiff, Glasgow, Liverpool, Newcastle-on-Tyne, Nottingham.

A circular letter from Blatchfords to customers.

see what else could be done by way of further patient care. Even as a young theoretician, Brian looked to be quite excellent. The main thrust of the development of the important Blatchford Stabilised Knee (BSK) was from 1954–5, but its early history is lucidly chronicled in a lengthy memorandum penned by Brian in January 1955. This was soon after he joined the family firm, and eight years before completion in 1963 of the premier development that made the name of Blatchford famous.

It was in response to an approach from the Ministry to the leg manufacturers on the Working Party Committee to come up with ideas for a stabilised knee for above-knee wearers, that Brian analysed the company's vision of the way ahead for the drum lock knee. This was a mechanism which offered the best braking and locking action, capable of carrying weight when required with the knee either extended or in a flexed position. At the time, the design and development of stabilised knees had been based on the logical reduction of effort following removal of certain basic necessities for stability of the conventional limb, and he candidly disclaimed complete knowledge of the mechanics of locomotion, whose fundamentals were still largely restricted to studies in the United States. A series of radiographs prepared by Ilford's Medical Radiology Department enabled a comparison to be made between action of the human knee and the 'Anatomic' direct friction knee centre movements of the most widely used continental types, the 'Striede' and 'Glider' knees. Blatchfords had kept an open mind on future progress, but faced with precipitate choice between hydraulic and mechanical means, the intricacy, delicacy and extreme precision of manufacture of the former inclined Brian against them. Always a realist, he noted that even if hydraulic design was suited to artificial limbs, the problems of leakage under stress if the limbs were not well designed meant that the company was not really in a position then to make so tricky an assembly, nor would the Ministry be prepared to pay for it. The main drift of company policy is that research is neither determined nor inhibited by costs, but at a time of relative uncertainty this was a criterion obviously to be kept in mind.

Ever a believer in the maxim, 'You can't sell if there's nothing to sell', Thompson shared Brian's dismay at the quality of limbs available to customers. Using to the full his talents as an outstanding publicist and diligent wooer of outside expertise, his many trips abroad were as much forays for fresh ideas as quests for companies desirous of materials. After forty years in the industry, he is an internationally recognised figure in the prosthetic world, especially in North America, and was seen by the company as a man of real stature, utterly reliable and responsible. In later years he became very much more than an employee, and as a director from 21 February 1964 onwards, he attended all Board meetings and was a confidante and friend to both W.A. and Brian.

Among other 1948 entrants, Ken Chick found the somewhat dark and dismal confines of 90 Clapham Road a rude awakening after the polished veneer and gleaming showcases at Desoutters. Given the chance to start in the fitting room at Roehampton, on the understanding that he completed a year in the workshop at head office, he reckoned the camaraderie was outstanding and discovered in W.A. a sort of father figure, strongly principled about money, direct and to the point. For George Bourdon, on the other hand, the transition from the elderly, strictly functional surroundings of Charles Salmon and Sons was no culture shock. He can look back over fifty years and more in the industry, and was the first employee to relocate with his family at Lister Road, Basingstoke. Amid a flood of memories, he recalls assisting Brian at some time in the late 1950s to 'pour our first foam, coloured black', for which preparation Brian 'borrowed' (his word) his mother's hand mixer from a kitchen drawer.

Responsible also for the supervision of branches and training of fitters, Thompson and Chick toured the centres at Reading, Cambridge, Portsmouth, Tunbridge Wells and Norwich on a day-visit basis. Reading was also covered one day a week, as were Portsmouth and Tunbridge Wells. Cambridge was once every two weeks and Norwich, in those days a tiresome seven-hour round trip, only once a month. A health service for all enveloped the British populace in 1948 and made disability less of a social malaise, but echoes from the recent past cling to anecdotes about the Blatchford self-measuring form, available from various outlets, half of them chemist's shops. One in particular stands out – a shop in Cambridge with three flights of stairs to be contemplated by even the most agile amputee, before a form could be traced, claimed and surreptitiously tucked away. Friendly and Benevolent societies still helped the needy, but more enterprising patients, unable to meet limb costs of, say, £12–£14, would go for sponsorship and take their completed forms round to major enterprises prepared to subsidise the disabled.

Ironically, although forty years on the national political character has changed from socialism to monetarism, such is the cyclical nature of politics that in spite of the egalitarian and centralisation beliefs of the post-War Labour government, emphasis for NHS supply by the limb industry at least was on the basis of vigorous competition. From Hangers, as it used to be, as well as Vessa, competition was always intense, and has never lessened. Indeed, at the outset of the NHS, the stranglehold on the market held by Hangers saw to it that Blatchfords had much ground to cover. Sales in 1948 of £27,450 more than doubled to £65,352 in November 1950, so that for the same time span a net loss of £1,252 was converted into net profit of £2,010. A Ministry of Pensions loan of £2,500 bolstered management morale but it remained a liability on the company, and annual financial performances wavered between the unimpressive and the downright dismal. A reversal to a net loss of over £3,000 in 1951, due primarily to the purchase of the freehold of 90 Clapham Road, gave cause for concern, particularly as total sales had also fallen by over £11,000 and a £5,000 overdraft stained the balance sheet.

Those were parlous days, made tenable only by a marriage of W.A.'s avowed intent to survive and the ability and stickability of his workmen. Long service members of staff readily call to mind how smaller items of hardware were purchased a box at a time from the shop across the road. Precious nuts and bolts were counted out upon specific request, and copper washers espied on the floor and worth only fractions of a penny were treated like gold dust and immediately retrieved. Chas's wine cellar had become a storehouse, and since surgical appliances still formed part of the cash flow, the unwary might find disconcerting a mass of round eyes, staring out of a box left where it ought not to be.

Price agreements inspired much angst among the small group of company decision-makers, boosted by the election to the Board of Brian in December 1952. Notwithstanding a small upward turn in 1952, a letter from W.A. to the Director of Contracts at the Ministry of Pensions in Blackpool, dated May of that year, strikes a very worried note. In it he urged an increase in prices, stressing the seriousness of a situation caused by the lack of new orders and general decrease in the financial stability of the

Rare surviving medals attesting to the skill of Chas. A. Blatchford, all pre-1916 in date.
(Graham Photography)

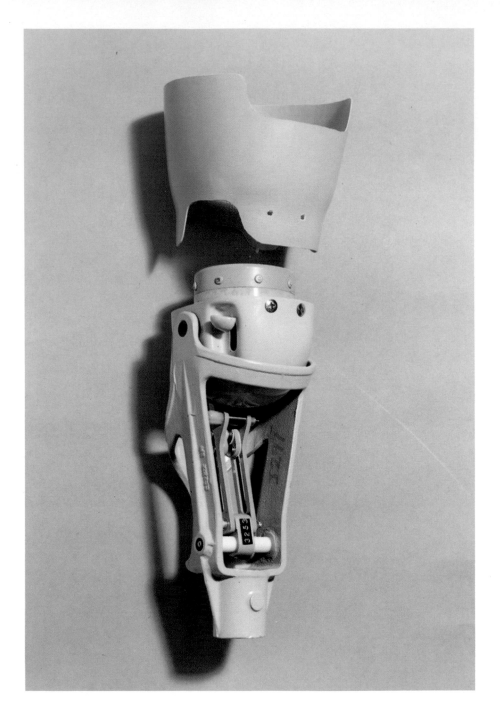

The PRIMAP variant of the Blatchford Modular Limb, widely available from 1970 onwards and familiarly known as the 'British MAP system'.

Brian receiving the Queen's Award for Technological Achievement from the Earl of Malmesbury, Lord Lieutenant of Hampshire.

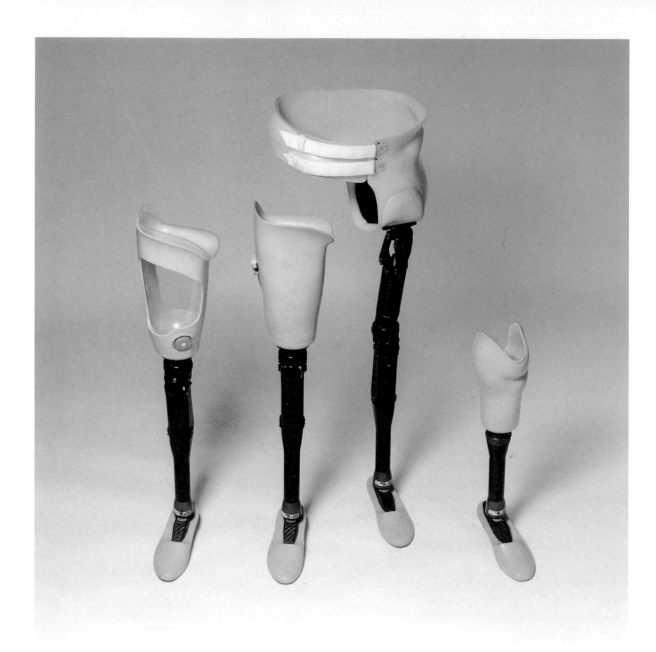

Endolite prosthesis for the above-knee, through hip and below-knee levels of amputation, shown without cosmesis covering.

company, especially with regard to future purchase of stocks of materials and continuance of the existing labour force.

The early years of the NHS involved much settling of contracts, not always the most pleasant of tasks, in that, as Bill Blatchford will vouch, contracts were often liable to fall through on unpredictables such as minor personality clashes with some local Ministry official. Bill was very much in a position to know, for in addition to a directorship held since February 1940, he had shouldered the duties of Company Secretary upon the retirement of A.G. Fettes in May 1954. In this position Bill proved a perfectionist, with an eye for detail, as painstaking as his predecessor, who, fortunately for the company, stayed on as a Board member until January 1959. Bill, in turn, made way in January 1964 for Group Captain Kenneth A. Jackman, a Chartered Accountant and partner in the firm of A.G. Fettes, Monkhouse & Co., the company's then auditors. Full of life and jollity, Jackman, as a sage financial and tax counsel, became almost a member of the family. With another lovely character in Thompson, Board meetings were often lively affairs. The provision of the Companies Act 1967 prevented Jackman from re-accepting the position, whereupon Joyce Blatchford took over as from the first Board meeting she attended, on 27 January 1968. Having joined the Board on 10 January 1973, she resigned the Secretaryship on 30 June 1974, stepping down in favour of Jackman, once more in harness after retirement from Messrs Ford Bull Ellis and Sales, the company's present auditors.

The Blatchford workforce has ever been enduring, staunch and cohesive. Long service and loyalty are qualities regarded by many as unlikely to be seen again, and in this age of labour mobility it may not be easy to find men as steadfast and conscientious as veteran woodworkers George Bourdon (1948–86), Ted Williamson (started in 1939), Len Bailey (1949 onwards), Jack Brewerton, a newcomer back in 1949, and Bill Shreeve (an employee from 1936 to 1987). They have their counterparts in the Metal Shop: Bert Norris (46 years with the company before retirement in 1982), Ron Heaphy (joined in 1938), Jim Church (from 1945), as well as George Page (1943) and his Assistant Foreman, Robert Parfett (also 1943).

Staff numbers and personnel remained unchanged for years, and for the older members of the firm general working conditions, notably wages, were very slow to develop. One repercussion of the first fitting course at Roehampton, when representatives of different companies within the industry met their co-workers, was a pay claim, obliquely described in a letter from the company to the Ministry of Health, dated 2 April 1959 and written shortly after the event. In response to a staff request to bring their salaries into line with those paid by the other limb makers, management felt the claim was justified and in accordance with the Fair Wage clause of contracts with the Ministry. At Clapham Road, active, militant trade unionism was unknown and negotiations took place through the foremen and office manager. Foremen such as Len Reid and David Forster were demi-gods, so the affair was doubtless conducted in a thoroughly gentlemanly manner. The increase would cost the company an extra £500 or so, but the responsibilities of the staff concerned could not be compared with those of others in the trade coming under the same heading. Fitters and higher executives at Blatchfords carried out additional duties; Roehampton fitters, for example, covered attendance at six other centres, besides carrying out the necessary alterations during the fitting to avoid limbs having to be returned to the factory. Certain of the branch fitters did likewise. The Manager and foremen, in addition to dealing with the normal business and manufacturing duties, undertook inspection and examination of all limbs prior to and after repair. This being so, it was agreed that salaries commensurate with their status should be awarded to:

A.E. Hawes, Manager
T.D. Forster, Foreman, Wood and Leather Department
L.C. Reid, Foreman, Metal Department
H. Thompson, Head Fitter (Roehampton)
K. Chick, Qualified Fitter (Roehampton)
A.E. Matthews, Progress and Production
F. Cameron, Qualified Fitter (Nottingham)
L.A. Scott, Qualified Fitter (Cardiff).

Earlier references to wages occur only as representations to the Ministry of reimbursement for increases agreed between the unions, supplemented by tables of new hourly rates. Inflation has made a mockery of figures quoted in the correspondence, but one submission from November 1954 is worth mentioning, if only because it was then that the pay of woodworkers, members of the National Union of Furniture Trade Operatives (NUFTO) was equalised with the rates paid to the metal workers.

At an extraordinary meeting of directors in January 1962, the shareholding qualification for company directors required by the Articles of Association was waived. This coincided with the first major changes in share ownership since the dispersal of the Steeper shares a decade earlier. Brian became majority shareholder, followed by Joyce and by Bill's wife, Valda. In May 1966 half of Brian's shares and all those belonging to Valda were placed in two trust funds for their respective children. Blatchford shareholders received a dividend for the first time in 1968, when it was disclosed that under the terms of the Finance Act 1965, a liability would arise for capital gains tax on the holdings of the two trust funds, either on the vesting date or on the fifteenth anniversary of the creation of the trusts, whichever date was earlier. To meet this liability it would be necessary for the trust to have an income, and this could only be achieved through the declaration and payment of a dividend.

By 1962, when the total staff was about a hundred, congestion at head office made the premises too small for the increased level of business. Total sales had clambered up over the previous five completed financial years from £85,324 to £137,702, and were likely to climb further, so something less Dickensian in appearance befitted both the company and its workers.

For those who knew Clapham Road only in its more utilitarian days, it may well have been a 'place of character which should never have been a factory'. To be fair, it was not purpose-built as one. When Chas. took over the lease of the house from a Miss Mary Ware on 7 March 1905, the schedule of deeds and documents dated back to June 1824, when Mr J.T. Taylor was leaseholder to one John Fentiman, Esq. (a nice social distinction). Almost immediately, on 1 May 1906, Chas. had a deed of covenant sent to the London County Council for alterations to the rear of the premises. Workshops were erected and a strip of land given up to road widening. It would appear that more extensive work was either in hand or contemplated in 1921, when planning consent was received for erection of a workshop building on the northern side of Richmond Terrace. Mindful that this building already existed, 'the works in question completed long ago', the company's solicitors pointed out its deviation from the plan approved back in 1905. The freehold was finally purchased by the company from W.A. in October 1951 for £8,000 and sold by mid-July 1964 for £27,000, a fair reflection of its value.

The house proper was light and airy, the upper floors initially the family home, although

Brian Blatchford, flanked by 'Tommy' Thompson (right) and John Shorter (left), together with design engineers and technicians in a corner of the R & D Unit, 1976.

after the Second World War these were partially given over to lodgers. In addition to W.A. as Managing Director, administration was supervised by an office manager and his secretary. There were no women on the permanent staff until after the war, when Blatchfords took on female staff as part of the general drift of women to work. Reception was very informal for the few customer patients, who might be met by the Managing Director himself and conducted into the hall through to the fitting rooms, which were basically the equivalent of drawing rooms.

The stores, receiving and despatch department was run by one man, but to cope with the post-NHS increase in work, the workshop staff was doubled. The cast room was packed to the ceiling, while in the next-door garden, leased by agreement with the owner, were stacks of timber. W.A. was an expert in the choice of wood and he would scour the country looking at trees, preferably stands of willow. Nearer home, the concrete floor of the workshop area was black with the dirt of ages past ground into it, and wire netting covered windows untouched intentionally by human hand.

101

A new factory in London was out of sight financially, so with overspill towns then in vogue, scouring of the countryside began afresh, both literally and figuratively. Unrestricted power to raise money on the company's assets by way of mortgages, bonds or debentures was conferred upon the Board in October 1962, and the company's bankers agreed in principle to provide suitable short-term finance. Action was taken to acquire freehold land on a newly built light industrial site in Lister Road, on the outskirts of Basingstoke. The situation was not only convenient for Roehampton but also enjoyed good road and rail connections. A struggle ensued to obtain freehold on an estate originally built by Messrs Percy Bilton on leasehold basis only, and Blatchfords only prevailed at the third attempt.

Green-field council-estate housing was another attraction, and about half the workforce opted for a new lifestyle, away from the metropolis and familiar surroundings. Applications, too, came in from metal and leather workers at Hangers and elsewhere. Niggling intervention in the shape of the Industrial Selection Scheme for new or expanding towns prompted a small flurry of memoranda, as did the insistence of the London County Council (LCC) and the local council that only people already living in council property would be re-housed. On 8 August 1963 the first party of eight workers, all from the PTB section, marched into the uncompleted building, led by George Bourdon. Only the wood machine shop was properly habitable, water was available from a single standpipe and the solitary toilet stood like a sentry box in the middle of a quagmire. By December the factory was in occupation and apart from minor teething troubles, no difficulties had been experienced.

Now properly ensconced in the brand new purpose-built factory at Lister Road, the meeting of the Board on 21 February 1964 was the first of a regular series of more formal gatherings instigated by Bill Blatchford. At this time the Board consisted of Bill as Chairman, W.A., Brian and 'Tommy' Thompson, the last named elected to the Board at this meeting. The reporting procedure for each meeting was agreed, and W.A. undertook responsibility for illustrative graphs showing total sales invoices in pounds, total materials purchased in pounds, total production of legs in units and total production of repairs in pounds. The first in a series of financial statements was presented by the Company Secretary, albeit only a rough estimate pending a more clear picture of the annual overheads at the new factory.

At the date of this meeting the management structure of the company was as follows:

Mr H. Thompson, Director and Manager of Branches; also responsible for liaison with the Ministry for fitting and orders
Mr K.A. Jackman, Company Secretary and Accountant
Mr A.E. Hawes, General Office Manager, with particular responsibility for trade work and special estimates
Mr T.D. Forster, Works Manager
Mr D.J. Lester, Assistant Works Manager
Mr A.E. Matthews, EID Manager, responsible for estimating, inspection, despatch, stores, order entry and progress chasing.

Hawes resigned for reasons of health on 31 December 1966, after which Matthews took over the responsibilities of Office Manager, including supervision of stores and costings.

The upheaval of the move had not affected production levels, but there was a large back-log of orders awaiting delivery. This was tackled branch by branch and by July much of the log

Brian and John Shorter head a group absorbed in watching some finishing touches to a MAP assembly.

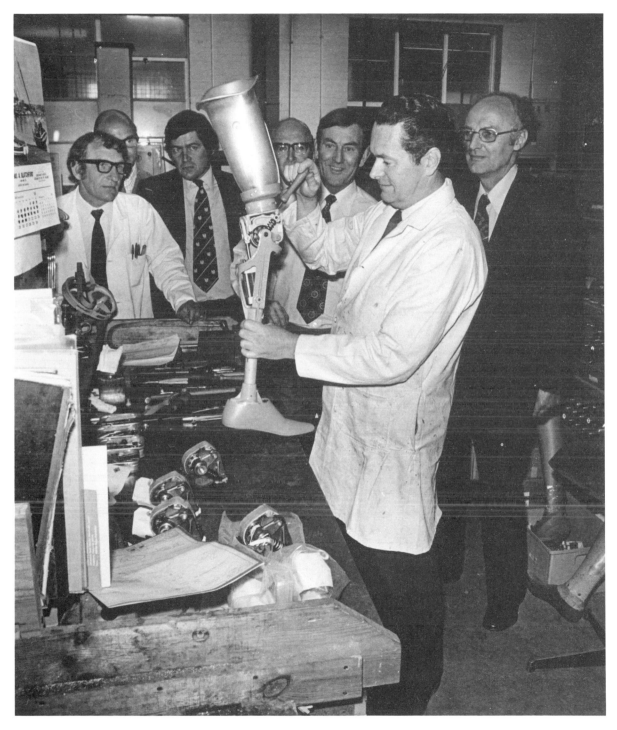

jam had been cleared, with production output at the time 112.5 per cent of input. The extra costs of opening the factory were underwritten by the Ministry and by July 1964 a substantial payment on account had been received. Payments for the increased overhead costs of running the factory continued for a time, until they were no longer justified by the volume of new business.

The total number of new legs across the country in early 1964 was reported as being 16,000 per annum, of which the company aimed for a maximum share of over 5,000. After four years it became possible to take stock. The figures showed that the company still had considerable leeway to make up.

Production year	New legs	Pylons	Repairs
1963	1,345	602	40,400
1964	1,550	678	48,800
1965	1,760	852	71,100
1966	1,898	1,192	75,800

A revival of interest in arm production flickered in 1964, sparked by a move by Hangers to enter this field under licence from a German firm. Brian and 'Tommy' Thompson linked attendance at a three-day conference in the United States concerning the use of powered arms with a visit to Germany for product evaluation. Figures and estimates of costs and likely turnover were passed to Jackman for assessment, and it was hoped to put together a prototype by the end of 1966. The continuing increase in leg orders overrode such considerations, and it was decided in September 1966 that the project was not feasible, but that preliminary studies based on sample arms from available components should persist. To free Brian's time to concentrate on projects of this nature, John Shorter was taken on as a draughtsman in March 1966. His experience in the aerospace industry was invaluable and he

was soon to prove his mettle.

There is every indication that a letter from the Department of Health to the British Surgical Trades Association, dated 14 January 1970, ventilated feelings about a change from contracts lasting three or more years to annual contracts, and the company's reaction was quick. Thompson suggested regular reviews of the situation so that at the end of five years the company would not find that those years had in effect constituted a period of five years' notice. Any reverberations from this quarter had to be treated with caution, not unmixed with respect, and toward the end of 1970, Bill, as Chairman, raised an important question of general policy. For a long time the company had been in a phase of expansion involving substantial capital expenditure, and he called for a period of consolidation with minimum capital outlay. The Board was fully in agreement but emphasised that there should be no curtailment of the expansion which affected private business, so far as this could be maintained with the present factory premises and equipment. Expansion, too, of the number of fitters and mechanics at existing branches should carry on.

In the early 1960s the firm produced artificial legs made on a conventional basis, but enhanced by the first major release of Brian's talent – the Blatchford Stabilised Knee (BSK). As a braking device for fast walkers and equally suitable for use on sloping surfaces, this pioneer British safety knee was the first truly innovative post-war development to make its debut for the company. Brian brought the full impetus of accumulated experience and logic to the first weight-activated knee-lock device produced in the world which was mechanically sound, and based on a simple principle. It was acclaimed as the only unit of its kind and has stood the test of time. Refinements continued throughout the 1960s, especially when a noise element, first noticed in mid-1965, needed to be remedied

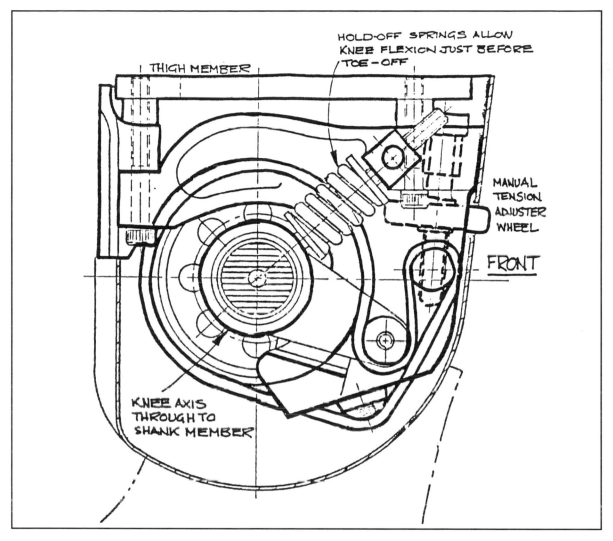

THIGH MEMBER

HOLD-OFF SPRINGS ALLOW KNEE FLEXION JUST BEFORE TOE-OFF

MANUAL TENSION ADJUSTER WHEEL

FRONT

KNEE AXIS THROUGH TO SHANK MEMBER

The Blatchford Stabilised Knee (BSK). A band-type mechanical weight-bearing knee brake, brought into play by the cumulative action of the swinging arm and offset brake-band anchor.

before its launch in the United States. In 1969, the duo of Thompson and B.G. Blatchford reached agreement with the United States Manufacturing Company (USMC) for the construction in the USA of the BSK under licence, on the basis of a lump sum for specifications and a royalty of 5 per cent on sales.

Another advance was British Patent 982,527, dated 3 February 1965, which offered an early Pneumatic Swing Phase Control Unit (PSPC) for knee flexion, while soon afterwards came a distinguished contribution from John Shorter (with Frank Webb) – the later version of the PSPC; British Patent 1,284,878, applied for on 2 December 1968 and then published on 9 August

Wally Nye and W.A. Blatchford (seated) demonstrate the locking strength of Wally's stabilised knee, even when only partially flexed. (A scene outside 90 Clapham Road in the late 1950s.)

1972. Based on an original idea of Professor Radcliffe of the University of California in Los Angeles, who also worked closely with Brian on design implementation, the PSPC was a two-valve pneumatic control device. Air flowed through one of the valves when the leg was flexing and through the other when the leg was extending. This enabled a different level of resistance to be set for both the flexion and extension motions of the leg, and the air in the cylinder also acted as a cushion at the end of the swing-phase of the limb. These three factors

combined allowed the amputee wearing a leg equipped with the PSPC to simulate the natural movement of the human leg.

The 1970s saw a flowering of patents, 11 in all. Each represented a quickening in progress, and they were designed to act as part of a brand new limb which, apart from the socket, used precisely engineered, interchangeable, pre-fabricated stock assemblies and components. This was Brian's Modular Assembly Prosthesis (MAP), the development of which began in the early 1960s, and the first of its kind available in the UK, although paralleled in Germany by the Otto Bock system. The philosophy behind the Modular Assembly Prosthesis represented a radical departure from previous limb types. The idea of being able to build a finished limb for a patient from a series of engineered sub-assemblies and components was new. This set of component parts was tailored to the individual patient's specification by constructing a limb to the right size and individually producing the socket for the patient and the shape of the cosmesis for the patient.

Brian's previous inventions were adapted to fit within this overall structure; the BSK becoming the main type of knee for the more active patient. The PSPC unit mentioned earlier was also incorporated within the MAP system, and combined with the BSK it provided an excellent functional prosthesis for the active amputee.

Also used within the MAP system was the uniaxial knee, which was used in conjunction with the first simple yet positive semi-automatic knee lock (SAKL), which locked more positively and safely than previous designs. Also available within the MAP system was the short knee chassis which allowed patients with a very long above-knee stump to benefit from the system. An internal kicker spring unit (ICS), which brought the limb back to the straight position without effort on the part of the

Diagram of the Pneumatic Swing Phase Control (PSPC) knee control device. Control of the piston was air-operated, in which a piston rod connected the piston to the upper leg member, and the resistance to the stroke in flexion and extension was separately adjustable.

amputee, was useful for some categories of patient for whom the PSPC unit was inappropriate.

The other revolutionary feature of the MAP system was that the alignment device was left permanently in the limb. In previous conventional limb construction the alignment was set at the time the patient was measured and could not be altered after the limb was made. With the MAP system the alignment could be altered at any stage as this part of the mechanism was left within the limb. This gave the prosthetist the ability to match the limb's alignment to the patient's changing needs.

A below-knee version of the MAP system was also available, bringing the advantages of a Modular Assembly Prosthesis to this level of amputation. This revolutionary limb system enabled a complete limb to be produced for a patient using fewer hours of skilled labour. Also the modular nature of the prosthesis enabled repairs to be easily performed upon it as the affected unit could simply be replaced.

Brian had completed testing the hardware so that the company was in the happy position of being able to offer firm proposals to the Department of Health just when it was considering limbs of modular type to help provide a more satisfactory service. The Blatchford MAP was compared for above-knee and below-knee amputees by the Department with two contemporary systems, one developed by Hangers (as was) and the other by BRADU (an official body, now the Bio-Engineering Centre). It was found to be at least 18 months ahead of its competitors; was approved to become the British Standard modular system,

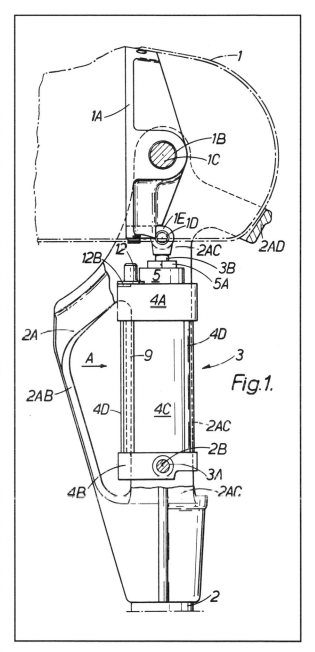

Fig. 1.

and, as the system most preferred by prosthetists and patients, was made available to all patients under the Department of Health and

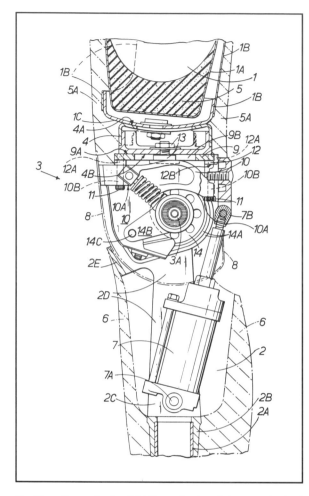

Section through the MAP as depicted in a technical drawing accompanying the Patent Specification.

For this design, the firm received in 1976 the Queen's Award for Industry in Technical Innovation, the Duke of Edinburgh Designer's Prize and the Design Council award, a unique triple.

In the opinion of Ken Chick, however, the brilliant engineering firm of Desoutters never realised how close it was to the modular system. Blatchfords' former Manager at Roehampton reminds one how renowned was their range of special portable tools, and how at the factory rows of enormous presses squirted metal up tubes by the 'dropped forge' method, to generate a sophisticated sequence of operations for knee and shin girders. Working on a consistency of exo-skeletal modules for easy interchanging, they were at least in the early stages of a semi-modular system, but had outpriced themselves and opted out of the NHS scheme at its inception.

Going back a few years, an infectiously animated report from Thompson enlivened the Board meeting of 19 September 1967, when he turned to the introduction of a new type of limb which would enable limbs to be assembled from stock parts. He went on to say that 'certain opposition had been expressed by BRADU and that there was a possibility that the Ministry of Health would be in a position to produce an alternative prototype within the next six years'. Brian and Thompson were unanimously of the opinion that the company should proceed with their existing MAP limb, regardless of lack of official enthusiasm, since it offered a much-needed improved service to the patient and would lend impetus to overseas sales. No great confidence was expressed in the ability of others to develop competitive systems, even in six years. But it was a pressure situation, and if Blatchfords were to outpace the competition, postponements and setbacks were unavoidable. By no means all were self-induced, for who could have foreseen the shock of a national

Social Security (DHSS) in July 1970. By 1972 it was proving its value in the field, and licence agreements were settled with all contractors for supply to DHSS patients. After a prolonged testing programme by BRADU and the Scientific and Technical Branch of the DHSS, to determine strength requirements and quality assurance, it emerged as a wholly viable and welcome system.

strike of limb-makers. The complex of contractual and costing negotiations was labyrinthine and stretched back to development arrangements for the BSK, at least to 1965. This was when Brian and his colleagues realised that it might become necessary for the company to set up its own machine shop to handle light engineering work.

Based on a rough estimate somewhere in excess of £10,000 for the cost of machine components, in September 1966 'Mr Jackman was asked to produce notes covering the financial and taxation advantages and dis-advantages of the formation of a new firm to handle production of machine parts, as compared with expanding Chas. A. Blatchford & Sons to include its own machine shop'. The die was cast that month when the Ministry ordered 12 sets of components for the MAP interchangeable leg to the value of £3,000. Once it had been accepted that the company needed its own machine shop, a large capital outlay was essential for the company's future operation, and with overdraft facilities provided, machinery for use on experimental production had been purchased by September the next year. The factory buildings were extended and additional staff taken on board.

Virtually from the outset, the Ministry's Supplies Division showed a genuine interest in using the MAP leg. After the 12 legs for initial trials had been supplied, a field trial of 50–100 was proposed. On the question of financing the MAP project, it was quite definite that no help would be forthcoming in the shape of direct disbursements from Ministry funds, but indirect assistance in the form of purchase from the company of parts for stocking the branches, up to a certain figure, was a move welcomed with relief. The company was still left with an awkward period when the multiple expense of enlarging the factory, providing the necessary plant, financing the MAP limb and meeting extra labour charges would leave it little short of a hand-to-mouth existence.

Hearn Engineering Limited, one of the company's major subcontractors for many years, had the first 100 sets of parts for the MAP legs ready by May 1968. They prepared the tooling and used this first batch as a proving ground for the tools. Anxiety to stay first in the field and honour delivery commitments in Sweden, Denmark and other continental countries meant bringing the programme forward as quickly as possible. Only thus could continuity of orders from the Ministry be assured, and there could be no deceleration of the programme of public-relations visits abroad. There was no disguising the frenetic pace of events, and an interim batch of 40–50 sets from existing sand castings was made ready for sale. By November 1968 all parts for the first 15 of the 100 initial MAP legs had been completed by Hearn, working in tandem with the company's now fully operational machine shop.

Feedback was positive in that reactions from British patients seemed to be favourable, and the sphere of overseas operations now encom-passed conferences, seminars and demon-strations in Belgium and Holland. A 'know-how' agreement and subsequent franchise was signed with the French company Proteor, on the basis of £1,000 lump sum and a royalty of £6 per limb produced, accepted by the French government on 1 January 1974.

Considerable interest but no commensurate flow of dollars stemmed from a visit to the United States in May 1969 by the now much-travelled sales duo of Brian and 'Tommy', and finance of the order of £27,500 to put MAP on schedule was beyond the company's means as 1970 dawned. Subventions of various kinds from the Department of Health were discussed in depth, and ultimately the decision was made to proceed on the basis that the Department would purchase the necessary tools to produce

Brian receiving the Duke of Edinburgh Designer's Prize, in 1976. This, together with a Design Council Award and a Queen's Award for Technology, was the first time any company had been so signally honoured in one year.

the MAP components, subject to a written proviso that Blatchfords retained sole use of them for work for the Department and for its private trade. The disappointing turnover figure of under half a million pounds for the year ended 30 June 1970 revealed the severe inroads made into the company's resources. Hidden costs for some ten thousand man hours lost from production and other expenses recoverable under the contract for the introduction of the

MAP system had yet to be charged.

Given the situation, the commencement of the first display of industrial muscle in the history of the industry could not have come at a worse moment. Large investment in new machinery coincided with a cash book debit balance of £12,000 compared with the overdraft limit of £25,000. It was cold comfort but sums due from the Department and non-payment of the men on strike would give a cushion so that several weeks could be weathered, if necessary, without recourse to a bridging loan. Management felt helpless, seething with impotence as the strike dragged on for eight weeks and two days, leaving export orders, deliveries and ways of meeting deliveries blown wildly off course. It was not a strike of Blatchfords' own choosing. Under the terms of the BSTA agreement with the craft unions, the 6 per cent increase due for payment on 1 September had been renegotiated to take account of exceptional rises in the cost of living. An increase of 12 per cent instead of 6 per cent had been accepted by the national executive, but rejected by the industry's labour force, who commenced unofficial strike action on 24 September. An increase of 13.45 per cent in production wages was eventually hammered out and the men returned to work as normal. In their absence, paper wages were still being calculated by non-striking office staff for the men to draw tax refunds, but, as Norah Smith recalls, the stillness of the factory was uncanny, almost eerie.

To deal with the back-log of orders arising from the strike, orders for new legs were suspended for a time, but as a result of the introduction of a temporary new bonus scheme, much of the shortfall was soon eroded, and on resumption of work the MAP programme was extended to a further three centres, making nine in all. The long-term effects of the cost of the strike were generously taken into account by the Department of Health, which reimbursed the company for any loss of profits arising from the strike, and also agreed to pay for the £30,000 expended up until the end of 1970 for increased staff costs over the contract allowance to do with the introduction of MAP.

Awareness of being highly in demand, and in possession of a head start with a highly desirable product in the MAP, lends an effervescence, a spring in the step, to the company's minutes of meetings throughout the 1970s. Bank balances showed considerable improvement and any challenges to patents would, in the right circumstances, be fought robustly. Although beholden to the Department of Health, any lingering hint of subservience was replaced by a dialogue between more or less equals. Premonitions, however, about the

conundrum presented by moves in Scotland emerged as early as 1971. In the light of the prevailing uncertainty about the situation there, although early rumours of 'nationalisation' smacked of speculation, Blatchfords preferred to wait until the full outcome of the Denny Report was known before showing its hand. Sales in 1971 had been £50,000, but if the Scottish provision of their service was to go independent, as seemed inevitable by 1978, 10 per cent of the company's business would be lost, putting at risk by the latter date a figure not far short of £250,000, nearly 40 per cent of the production wage bill.

W.A.'s death in August 1971 furnished reminders of anxious years in the late 1930s, when his endeavours alone held the company upright and provided the grounding for its present success. Best remembered as a 'backroom boffin', mad keen on mechanical devices, he also had a special feel for an older medium, wood, and when approached in the 1960s by a major stocking manufacturer, with the request that Blatchfords create for them five wooden legs exact to specifications of circumference and curvature, it was W.A. who personally carved with a spokeshave every centimetre down the legs, perfect in every detail, and all for £100.

In view of Jackman's retirement, scheduled for April 1974, it was felt that the long-term financial direction of the company would gain enormously by the appointment of someone suitable for training as a future Financial Director, able to handle all matters of finance under the Board's direction. Such matters would include general accounting, with books up to trial balance stage, payroll, setting up a cost accounting system, day-to-day contract negotiations with the Department, and much more, but all well within the province and capacity of the appointee, Tony Rainbird, who joined the company in 1974.

A special Board meeting was called on 11 April 1972 to discuss the supply of Blatchfords' MAP to Hangers. To set the scene, at a meeting with the Department of Health on 2 December 1971, it was made crystal clear that as far as possible there would only be one type of leg in the foreseeable future, and that would be of modular construction. A committee under the chairmanship of Professor Sir Andrew Kay had also been set up to advise the Minister on future research and development for all aids to the disabled under the NHS. The committee's first report was prepared but was leaked. As a result the report was not published and the committee was scrapped. A more or less permanent committee (ACRAL) was then formed under the chairmanship of Professor Kay. The recommendation of this committee, in conjunction with the British Orthopaedic Association, with regard to lower limb amputees, was that the Blatchford modular system should be prescribed by all surgeons and should be available to all contractors for the period before the production of the second generation MAP. Reverting to Hangers, and working on known types of amputees, it appeared the figure would be in the order of 200 sets of MAP components per week, and the assumption was that the proposition most acceptable to Hangers would be to give permission to their parent company, the Tilling Group (formerly the Vokes Group), to do all the work for their own use only, on a small royalty basis. The position of the Department was a stand-off in that they wanted other contractors to supply the Blatchford MAP but regarded it as a purely commercial arrangement, and, provided there was no transgression of their basic ideas, outside their purview. Formal discussions began between the parties in the first quarter of 1972, and it appeared likely that Hangers would require 1,800–2,000 sets of components in the first year. The DoH wanted the contract period to be

extended for longer than one year, a reasonable enough reaction provided prices could be reviewed at the end of each year. The Department also agreed to pay a £2 royalty for each leg supplied over three years. A draft agreement was thrashed out at an important meeting on 6 October 1972 with the Tilling Group, whereby they would be allowed to make all the parts they wanted and Blatchfords would supply specialised castings, forgings and other materials. In return, a lump sum of £5,000 would be paid for drawings and a royalty of £100,000 paid over three years, commencing 1 October 1972. Part of the package was a training programme for a selected number of Hangers' personnel. Delays in the supply of MAP to Tilling were caused by fine-print details inherent in the setting up of a holding company, HVK (Hanger Vessa Kelly) Limited. The licensing agreement was looked at anew in December 1975, when the client asked for a reduction in the grant to 12 months only. Blatchfords counter-proposed that instead of the existing £100,000 for three years, the figure for 1976 should be £50,000, quite unrelated to the number of limbs produced, and that this proposal should be forwarded to the Department.

Having seen sales to the Department bounce from £490,328 in the year ended June 1971 to £829,182 in the splendid year 1971–2, the company then surpassed itself when the accounts for the year ending 30 June 1973 showed that for the first time turnover had topped the £1 million mark. No sooner had the rejoicing died down than the New Year Honours List gave cause for further celebration. Brian became the first person in the history of the limb-making business to receive royal recognition with the award of an MBE for his years of dedicated service to others. Further family matters were raised when, after an Extraordinary General Meeting of the Board, authority was given in December 1975 for capitalisation of the company's shares to 200,000, a figure deemed more realistic than the 10,000 which had made up the share capital since 1926.

In accordance with the Department of Health's programme for rationalising centres, branches at Carlisle, Bristol, Oxford and Leeds were closed on 1 January 1973. Cardiff and Swansea branches closed at the end of December 1977, paradoxically for Cardiff the year of its diamond jubilee as the pioneer Blatchford branch, outliving by just half a dozen years its founding father and first Manager, the then youthful, moustached W.A. At Newcastle, about 400 Vessa patients came over to Blatchfords on 1 January 1978, followed on 14 January by 130 at Preston from Stubbs, both moves demanding the employment of extra technicians. Any loss of business was more than compensated for by the opening of the Stanmore Centre on 1 February 1976, with sufficient capacity for 25–30 men and 2,800 patients over its first two years. Blatchfords became the sole contractors and HVK the sole contractors at a second new centre, Harold Wood. A great deal of Thompson diplomacy and strategic planning went into the setting up of Stanmore, consolidated by adroit management by Peter Lewis through some testing times. Stanmore's reputation as one of the leading orthopaedic hospitals in the country made it essential that the venture should be successful and 'it was felt that it would be interesting for us to get into the Orthotic field'. An opportunity to put this interest to good use occurred when the company made 10 sets of clamps and 50 sets of joints on behalf of Brian Meggitt, in charge of the Accident Unit at Cambridge, to give form and body to his idea for a fracture brace kit. More visionary in scope, an internal company committee was set up late in 1976 to investigate the chances of establishing a partnership with an orthopaedic surgeon and possibly a clinic with ancillary staff for the supply and fitting of private limbs and orthotics.

Emphatic pointers to an expansionist, high-tech future, with concern for the increasing need for research into customer reaction, are discernible as the new decade loomed and with it the second generation MAP. Computerisation of various procedures had been presaged by the presence at a Board meeting on 11 August 1977 of Stephen Blatchford, invited to give a summary of the position concerning computer hardware. Another Thompson suggestion, that 'we run our own meeting inviting selected people, e.g. the DHSS, Graham Hart, Roy Dean, a Surgeon, Brian Meggitt, John Angel, and perhaps some others such as Gunnar Holmgren and Rene Verdonck', to ascertain precisely what was wanted in the new MAP, found a receptive ear at the Department. Then came Brian's considered opinion that whereas the first MAP was designed for this country only, an 'international leg' should be a target, at the most competitive price possible. To keep prices down manufacture would have to be on a larger scale, and while this would involve the company in considerable tooling expense, capital expenditure would be justified by a worldwide market.

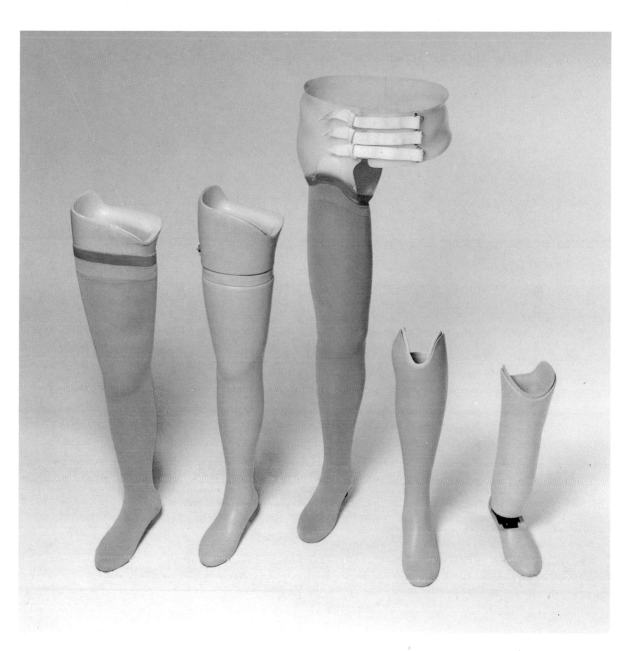

Thermoplastic sockets and continuous shaped foam fairing for the Endolite range, with fabric outer stocking or skin cover.

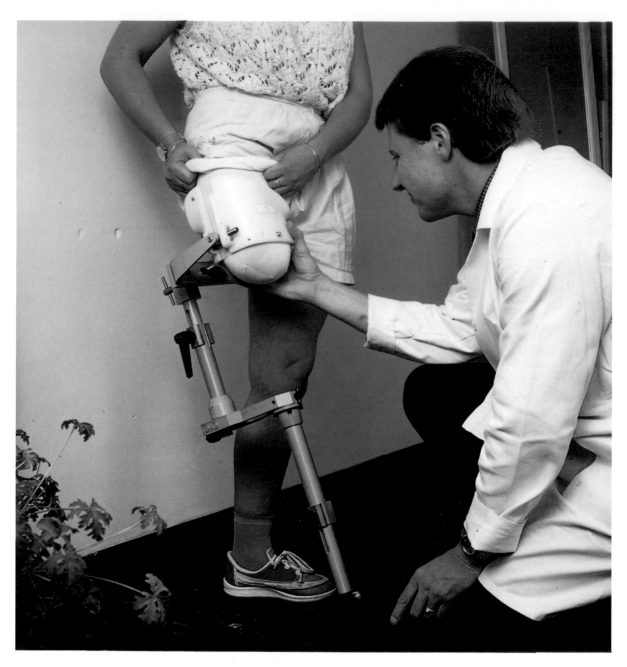

A sensitive approach combined with the application of good prosthetic practice in fitting an Endolite above-knee limb.

Learning to walk is part of the bond between prosthetist and patient.

THE QUEEN'S AWARD FOR
TECHNOLOGICAL ACHIEVEMENT
1976

The company received a Design Council Award, a Queen's Award for Technology for the MAP system and Mr Brian Blatchford was awarded the Duke of Edinburgh's Designer's Prize. This was the first time that any company had received these three prestigious awards in one year.

CHAPTER EIGHT

Into the 1990s

Expansion with Endolite

In January 1981 Brian made the momentous decision that since it was uniquely their own design, Blatchfords should not be in a hurry to let other contractors have Endolite components. If and when it became generally available, the company would take on the supply of components and not, as in the past, grant licences for the manufacture. The DHSS wanted the best system available for their patients and were keen to bring Endolite forward as quickly as possible. Therefore it was arranged in June 1982 that when Endolite was ready for distribution, Blatchfords would manufacture Endolite rather than grant licences to other companies in England. In common with the introduction of new technology everywhere, Endolite implied that new staff needed to be taken on with the right background to produce the components, sales for which were going much faster by February 1985 than expected.

The emphasis on Endolite was paramount and nothing was to hinder its promotion from the outset as a complete limb system for the rehabilitation of the patient, and also as a design philosophy for the manufacture of the limb. After the company's experience in producing its first-generation Modular Assembly Prosthesis – the MAP system – it now desired to produce a

second-generation modular system that met the requirements set down by clinicians at the Ascot meeting in 1972. This meant that the total system for an above-knee patient should weigh around 2 kg and for a below-knee system around 1 kg. Building on its commitment to design and materials testing, Blatchfords was to invest time and financial resources in a search for the answer.

The whole design therefore of Endolite was oriented towards producing a lightweight limb system. It became clear in the earlier stages of the development cycle that the use of existing materials would not be sufficient to meet these new reduced weight limits. Brian and John Shorter accordingly began investigating the use of modern materials, particularly carbon-fibre plastics – as used in the aerospace industry – to find a way of manufacturing a complete shin assembly using this material in an economic manner. The fabrication expertise of the Atomic Energy Research Establishment at Harwell played an early part, but, more importantly the company's own R&D breakthroughs which gave birth to Endolite have allowed Blatchfords to retain a several-year lead in this field.

Once a method for reducing the overall weight of the limbs was discovered, the next step was to incorporate the existing functional

elements of the MAP system into the new lightweight system without sacrificing these weight advantages. It was clear to the design team that the new limb system should have a continuous cosmetic fairing, rather than having a break at the knee. This approach was rigorously supported by the DHSS. This meant that the size of the functional elements of the limb would have to be miniaturised to sit within a foam cosmesis. Brian therefore returned to the design of the BSK, which consisted of a brake band working round the outside of a drum element, and considered whether it would be possible to reverse this arrangement so as to have a brake band expanding outwards on the inside of a drum. If this were possible, then the

Soon after being fitted with a CAT-CAM socket on his Blatchford Endolite prosthesis, 25-year-old Mark Durling was able to enjoy a game of squash.

overall braking area could be maintained but the size of the complete unit would be considerably reduced. Thus was born the ESK – the Endolite Stabilised Knee – which reproduces the functions of the older BSK but in a far smaller and lighter unit. These objectives have been achieved without detracting from international strength and durability requirements, so that for below-knee patients fast-action sports such as squash can be a reality. Other segments of the MAP system came under the same scrutiny – a cheaper and more lightweight version of the

Mark Durling, who lost his leg in a motorcycle accident, demonstrates how the Endolite limb may be flexed more than 90 degrees.

PSPC, the SAKL and other units were produced to fit within the Endolite make-up.

It was also felt that insufficient attention had been paid to the question of the foot action on previous limb systems, as the MAP used a similar foot to previous conventional limbs. Feedback from amputees indicated the need for a foot that would accommodate to any uneven terrain encountered while walking, which meant that the foot should be able to move in any direction to allow this movement. This design specification led to the birth of the Multiflex foot and ankle, a beautifully simple creation which matched the needs of the patient and made everyone wonder 'Why on earth didn't we think of this before?' It consisted of a simple ball joint arrangement at the natural ankle level coupled with a snubber rubber

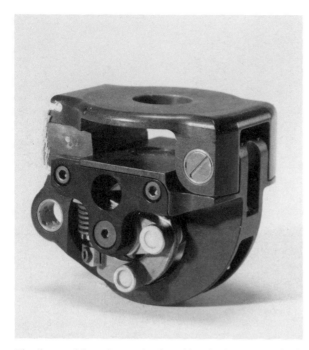

The 'bouncy' knee has a simple rubber built into it, which can be seen here (top left) underneath the plate at the top of the knee which aligns the knee with the thigh.

Although suitable for all types of patients when introduced into service during 1983–4, more recent developments have refined the functionality of the limb, so that Endolite represents the first modular artificial leg offering optimum use to sedentary patients as well as young, active or heavier amputees. In particular, the following additions to the range became available.

The Bio-Engineering Centre at Roehampton, part of University College, London, developed what they called a 'bouncy' knee using the company's MAP system. This was an addition to the BSK which enabled the limb to flex slightly during the stance phase of walking to produce an even more natural gait. The company produced a refined version for Endolite which works particularly well with the ESK and, as well as the advantages outlined above, also gives some cushioning at the knee during the walking cycle. The range of Endolite knees was also extended to include a manual knee-lock version of the stabilised knee, aimed particularly at new amputees still uncertain of their capabilities. They can either rely on the stabilised knee, or if they have not yet built up sufficient confidence during the first few months of trial, they can manually lock the leg straight.

The Endolite system was further extended to include a prosthesis for the through-knee and through-hip amputation levels. These are both designed around the idea of using a four-bar linkage, which has the benefit of moving the centre of rotation away from the mechanism itself so that in a through-hip case the rotational axis can be placed above the mechanism at the natural level of hip movement. This leaves the through-hip wearer a longer stride length, which again produces a more natural gait.

These additional refinements to Endolite mean that it is now a very compliant system: it has a multi-axial ankle mechanism which can

which provided different degrees of resistance in the various directions of movement. The overall hardness of the ankle could be set to suit the various lifestyles of patients.

Having designed the main elements of a lightweight high-technology limb system for both above-knee and below-knee patients, the design team turned its attention to the way that sockets should be produced. It would be a shame to throw away the advantage of this new lightness by using old conventional heavy sockets, so a new way was devised of making sockets from thermoplastic materials, draped over a plaster model of the patient's stump. This provided the final element of the jigsaw and enabled the complete Endolite system to provide the full function that a patient needs at an extremely light weight.

absorb shocks in all directions, a bouncy element at the knee which again will cushion loads to the patient, and for the through-hip amputation level an energy-storing mechanism is being introduced. The combined effect is to reduce the energy the amputee has to use to walk with the leg, making Endolite an extremely easy to use solution for patients. They can be unaware of having an artificial leg and are able to return to cycling, running, even mountaineering and rock climbing.

A new four-bar through-knee version of Endolite will also be available shortly. This is designed to be adjustable for both active and less active patients by adjusting the geometry of the four-bar linkage. It is designed to have the minimum possible protuberance on the bottom of the long through-knee stump and can also work with the standard PSPC, ICS and SAKL units. It represents a major step forward in the capability of through-knee limbs for the amputee.

A firm proposal for the phasing-out of the older MAP system over a three-year run-down period was agreed with the other contractors and the DHSS in mid-1985. At an important meeting with the same body in July 1985, Endolite supply was talked through and a proposal was put to the company that Blatchfords should supply it at all of its 12 centres; Cossins and Stubbs at their centres in Manchester, Sheffield and Leeds, at two of which Blatchfords also figures; Vessa at remaining centres where there was no company representation; and Hangers to supply at those centres where they were the sole contractor.

Agreement to purchase CNC equipment to produce the revolutionary Endolite system in-house was made in November 1983, but another 18 months elapsed before delivery was completed and the machinery fully up and running. The asking price in 1983 for the Deckel DC30 Machine Centre and a Gildermeister

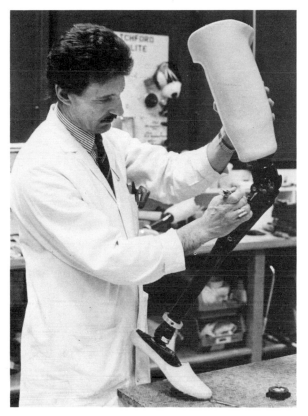

Checking the operation of a knee mechanism on a Blatchford Endolite carbon fibre prosthesis. The Endolite system currently incorporates fourteen functions at the knee which can be selected to suit the weight and activity of amputees within all age groups. An integral part of the Endolite system is the Multiflex foot with its ingenious ankle joint which enables the foot to accommodate to uneven ground conditions.

Turning Machine was £195,000 for the pair, but a 'SEFIS 2' grant reduced the cost to £130,000. Tony Rainbird, Financial Director and Company Secretary, calculated that utilisation could be as low as 45 per cent and still justify purchase of the machines with the grant taken into account. In 1984 the company had acquired new and additional factory premises at Unit F1, Grafton Way, Basingstoke. The engineering shop for the

Mark Durling emulates Greg Mannino running leg over-leg with an Endolite.

sophisticated manufacturing equipment necessary to produce Endolite became operational by the end of the year. Traditional stock became obsolete faster than anticipated and transfer of production work to F1 started early in 1985, along with carbon fibre operations and all Endolite pre-production work.

The Special Policy Group set up within the DHSS to administer the findings of the separate Government-appointed committee, chaired by Professor Ian McColl (later Lord McColl of Dulwich), sought an increase in the supply of Endolite components by 50 per cent above the 1986 level and the demand was such that only by moving stores to F1, at an estimated cost of £70,000, and running the CNC equipment in two shifts, could Blatchfords raise the tempo. Two more CNC machines were ordered in March 1989 and installation of this advanced computer-controlled technology has shown its capacity for great versatility, flexibility and accuracy in the production of components for 17,000 limbs a year, of which 5,000 are made by the company. To keep up with demand and maintain equilibrium at the main factory, decentralisation of Endolite manufacture began, starting with Manchester, ahead of the DHSS insistence in agreement with McColl, that the majority of limb work should be at the Artificial Limb and Appliance Centres (ALACs), away from the central factory. A flavour of the company's many-faceted activities, all poised around Endolite development, can be detected from a pot-pourri of 1986 technical activities:

PRILITE – fully tested and approved
Patent adjustable ankle – 75 per cent limb-tested
Through-hip disarticulation – 50 per cent tested
Symes – prototype under test
Through-knee – to be produced as prototype

The first Research and Development Unit (R&D) was set up by Brian in a 3,000 sq. ft leased factory at Kempshott Park. This was in 1973 when rapid MAP development necessitated a Drawing Office and Experimental Workshop with at least some elbow room. At this stage, however, mass production in so distinctive an industry was some way off, but as the MAP programme thrived and expanded, rapidly earning an international reputation, new premises had to be found and R&D was transferred to the U6 facilities at Sherrington Way, near Lister Road. In the manufacture of modular limbs all components and assemblies are fully laboratory-tested to international standards set at the Philadelphia Conference of 1977, and quality control is assured by inspection checks at all stages of assembly. It continues to flourish and a recent advance is the Prosthetic Research Centre at Basingstoke District Hospital. As far back as July 1980, a visit by Department of Health officials suggested that a small fitting facility at Basingstoke would be a good idea 'when the financial stringency was over'. A decade later, after expressions of interest from the local hospital in the setting-up of a clinic within its premises, fulfilment came closer when in 1988 the Disablement Services Authority (DSA) approved a Clinic and Centre of Excellence. Legal formalities indicative of the company's initiative and financial backing were completed in June 1989, and in tandem with the renewed vigour and professionalism evident at the branches, the showplace Blatchford Prosthetic Research Centre was formally opened by Lord Holderness, Chairman of the DSA, and himself a double amputee.

The Old Order Changes

In discussion about the future of the limb industry, minuted in October 1982, 'Tommy'

Thompson questioned whether, as national policy evolved, limb fitting would feature in the company's organisation. Both he and Brian went back a long way in the industry and hard experience gave them a prescience about change. Nevertheless, it was a portent of things to come when Brian replied that all indications presaged a greater element of 'competition', which could only be to the company's advantage. In some ways Endolite acted as a catalyst, and debate surrounding where and how expansion would be possible remained open-ended when, in early 1984, the old order began to change. The death of Ken Jackman, aged 81, deprived the Board of an infectiously cheerful and positive financial adviser and friend. 'Tommy' Thompson's 65th birthday soon afterwards meant he could continue to work only part time, although the Chairman felt the company had greater need than ever of his keen discernment to neutralise the loss of Jackman. Engineering specialist, John Shorter, joined the Board on 1 September 1984, with special responsibility for R&D. Tony Rainbird was already an indispensable part of the Board, carrying a workload that had long outgrown the parameters laid down for the job as given during three gruelling interviews in 1973.

As Christmas 1985 approached, the company was smitten by a cause for widespread grief, and many are the expressions of sorrow still to this day over the death of a Managing Director for whom work was 'doing my hobby'. Brian Geoffrey Blatchford passed away on 24 December and with him departed a great talent for designing improved artificial limbs, and, as a superb theorist, latterly in directing the efforts of others to do the same. He was a quiet man, not given to saying a great deal, but someone whose capacity for caring embraced more the welfare of people entrusted to him than any notions of company profitability. Brian fostered the steady growth of the firm largely through his deep

knowledge and long experience, preferring to leave detailed management of the company to his executives. Such was his introspection and sensibility that Thompson used to ask him regularly how large Blatchfords was intended to be, and often the Managing Director had to be persuaded to turn his mind to the matter of extra income and where it was to come from.

In his memory, the Brian Blatchford Memorial Prize was accepted by the ISPO, with the proviso that candidates should come from the wider realms of prosthetics and orthotics, rather than just prosthetics.

The Board minutes for 31 December 1985 merely record that 'Stephen Blatchford was appointed Managing Director in place of his father. His appointment will provide the assurance that the Blatchford family will continue to take an active part in the running of the company.' Like all such minutes, this was typical understatement, for Stephen's assumption of the position was premature and dictated by circumstances. There was manifest staff relief at the continuation of the firm rather than a take-over, but as will be seen, a series of hammer blows shook the company's composure before the next year was out. At first an unknown quantity to his senior managers, Stephen introduced a radically new managerial style. Direction from the top was more marked, and with it came database information storage and retrieval, long-range planning and anticipation of market forces. Instead of producing primarily finished limbs, the company began selling more in the way of component parts, a prime factor in the noticeably different shaping of its corporate structure. Technical expertise, for all that, lies in the genes, and to Stephen's financial acumen has been skilfully woven a more than presentable newcomer's awareness of what constitutes a good design.

The industry grapevine was fairly vibrating

The Rt. Hon. the Lord Holderness PC DL, Chairman of the Disablement Services Authority and himself a double leg amputee, met Miss Samantha Ellis, also a double leg amputee, after he had formally opened the Blatchford Prosthetic Research Centre at Basingstoke District Hospital. Miss Ellis is fitted with an advanced design of stump socket known as CAT-CAM which incorporates a flexible inner liner for improved comfort on her lightweight Blatchford Endolite above-knee artificial legs. Lord McColl of Dulwich, Director of Surgery at Guy's Hospital (right) looks on.

with well-informed rumours about the likely findings of the McColl inquiry into the state of the artificial limb services, and lightning changes had to be made to the management structure so as to give Stephen room to

manoeuvre. John Shorter assumed responsibility for marketing and a Personnel Manager was recruited, reporting to Tony Rainbird. Eddie Gane assumed full responsibility for the branches as of 1 March 1986, sparing the 26-year-old Managing Director one less burden as he squared up to his first instalment of that long-running serial encounter, the next round of DHSS contract negotiations. Chivvying from the DHSS was a fact of life that the Board was used to and could deal with; co-existence with public-sector budgetary authorities over almost four decades had become second nature. Through no fault of his own, however, just as Stephen embarked upon his new role, dealings between the two parties took on a keener edge, the limb makers overall being seen to be adopting a self-

123

vindicatory, defensive attitude, forced upon them by rapidly unfolding events.

The McColl Review and its Aftermath

When it appeared, the two-volume *Review of the Artificial Limb and Appliance Centre Services* was far more critical of the limb and wheelchair services than had generally been expected. The fruit of much endeavour on the part of the inquiry team chaired by the outspoken and fiercely independent Ian McColl, Professor of Surgery at Guy's Hospital, the survey illuminated one of the more concealed corners of the DHSS, and not everyone exposed to the harsh glare of publicity was exactly enamoured of its findings. Published in February 1986, after a period during which rumours abounded, the report was a forthright account of a service which, in the view of various pressure groups and concerned individuals, left a lot to be desired. The interests of the consumer were placed foremost and hardly any area was spared – including Professor McColl's own; 37 per cent of amputations, it pointed out, could have been better done. Injured servicemen, for whom the national limb service was created in 1915, today constitute a small minority of those treated, and as the table of referrals indicated, most of the 63,000 people now using the limb services suffer from diseases of advancing years and need diverse medical and social services.

The figure of 5,000, after natural attrition, has been constant for many years, leaving Blatchfords only moderate room for expansion in the mid-1980s, counterbalanced, of course, by the increasingly influential technological nature of the company's business. Hence it could be said that a modicum of disagreement could be attached to the claim in the McColl Report that the service in Britain had not moved with the

Referrals for artificial limbs in England, Wales and Northern Ireland, 1986.		
Reasons for amputation	*Leg*	*Arm*
Vascular insufficiency	3,447	14
Diabetes	1,064	2
Trauma	383	138
Malignancy	189	31
Congenital	36	93
Others	190	9
Total	5,309	287

times and had failed to keep pace with developments abroad, as the company was in advance of the world in its technology.

In the Committee's opinion, three major faults were found in the ALAC service, then run by the DHSS with headquarters in Russell Square, London, via 18 main centres and nine satellites across England and Wales. It chose as its first criticism the complacent attitude of those responsible for the low standard of fitting: 'Too many amputees are given ill-fitting limbs which cause unnecessary pain and suffering. Many factors can be responsible, particularly mistakes in construction, inappropriate amputation, poorly organised handling of the patient and inadequately trained prosthetists.' The Report stated that part of the problem lay in the training of prosthetists. Scotland had a course at Strathclyde University but nothing equivalent had yet been established in England although the London School of Prosthetics was in fact up and running, but not visited by McColl. The second major fault lay with management, whose failures created serious delays in delivery times and an ineffective use of resources. The evidence from the disabled revealed their inability to exercise consumer power. People who had endured the shock of losing a limb were then being dealt a second blow as they waited, often in vain, for a comfortable, well-fitted artificial limb. Equally impotent was the Department of Health, seen as incapable of controlling the 'costs, prices or profits' of the close-knit ring of suppliers. Contractual arrangements which resulted in a near-monopoly in the supply of limbs were also attacked. It has to be said, by way of mitigation, that neither the Department nor the companies themselves found the situation satisfactory, but as the *Guardian* remarked on 17 June 1987, over a year later, 'nobody mentioned choice'. Six companies supplied limbs, three of which were owned by one parent company, and the working party wanted to see a break in the monopoly, opening supply to the smaller firms or getting artificial limbs from abroad. The Report's central recommendation was for a new management board, chaired by someone experienced in business, to take over the running of the service, thereby ensuring revitalisation of research and development programmes, new training and upgrading of prosthetists, and an increased emphasis on rehabilitation. The Report's conclusion was dramatic: 'only a total break with the current organisation...could jolt these services into the state of caring efficiency which is required'.

Blatchfords made written and oral submissions to both the Review Board and its Working Party, and received a visit from the former on 1 October 1984. Given the firm's proven track record since moving to Basingstoke, little wonder that it took umbrage at what seemed a tendency in the *Review* to conveniently lump together all the contractors 'as a whole' when it came to shortcomings, ignoring the characteristics which made Blatchfords so different. An influence on the growing climate for change was the dismissal by Hangers in September 1986 of 300 bench-hands after a long-drawn-out dispute. Life had become a struggle for patients whose limbs

were on the point of near-collapse and, with replacements slow to arrive, many voiced their resentment at their mobility being reduced, not by increasing infirmity but for industrial reasons. Despite a delivery time 'second to none' – one of the disciplines demanded by McColl – and 'the most up to date high technology model limb on supply to the DHSS' (letter from Brian Meacock, *The Daily Telegraph*, 12 May 1987), Blatchfords wanted none of the log jam diverted to them from Hangers, since it would affect the special relationship enjoyed with their own patients, clearly the first priority. Predictably, the Committee's findings drew fire from the manufacturers, and a spokesman for Hangers – which with Vessa and Kellie was owned by the InterMed Group (itself part of BTR) and supplied 78 per cent of all patients with lower limbs – replied that the British limb service was better than anything on offer overseas and 'McColl's conclusion that a quango is needed to run the service is contrary to the evidence'. A survey commissioned by the DHSS and published in January 1984 had shown a high proportion of people satisfied with the service they received, whereas the McColl Report was only about the ones who were dissatisfied.

As a result of the McColl call for a new central authority to supervise the industry and transfer ALACs into a modern integrated rehabilitation service, in April 1987 John Major, then Minister for Social Security, announced a drastic shake-up. Eventual control of the ALAC was to pass from the civil service to individual regional health authorities. In the interim, a new special health body, the Disablement Services Authority, was created on 1 July 1987 to take over from the DHSS all responsibility for running the existing ALACs. Under the chairmanship of Lord Holderness, the Board of the DSA's composite blend of experts in disability or commerce gave it the depth of experience to develop and improve these services. Although funded by the Department, it reports directly to the Health Service Management Board, but is seen to have transitory powers only, planning, in co-ordination with the regional health authorities, the integration of all services into those of the NHS on 1 April 1991. With the NHS Procurement Directorate, it has since decided that a Centre of Responsibility should be set up in Sheffield, responsible for orthotics and prosthetics, to take over from the DSA in 1991. During discussions with the DSA about the new contracts, Lord and Lady Holderness, Lord McColl and Melvyn Jeremiah visited Basingstoke in July 1987. Lord Holderness changed contractors to Blatchfords for supply of two Endolite below-knee limbs as replacements for his previous metal substitute legs.

Echoes from the past surfaced in January 1988. A complaint by surgical trade leaders that a report by BBC TV's consumer programme, *That's Life* , in July 1986, on problems within the limb service was misleading and unfair 'in the extreme' was rejected by the Broadcasting Complaints Commission. Despite 'omissions and inaccuracies' which should have been avoided, the Commission ruled that the programme had been in the public interest and the inaccuracies were not so serious as to make the whole item unjust and unfair. In this centenary year only one observation need be made and that is, whatever the political realities, Blatchfords had not been immune to the fervour that gripped the nation when the Falklands Task Force set sail, and when the dozen amputees came home with a crying need for substitute limbs, right across the industry their needs were put first.

The pair of words, competition and choice, are by no means novelties in this chapter, and concern was still being expressed, not least in the national press, that the real problem – lack of choice – was one which Government Ministers had been slow to address. Until competition could be introduced, it was alleged that little was seen to be done to release the limb suppliers' grip on business, nor any sign of independence for the limb-makers in their employ. Rumoured complaints about the continuing inability of new companies to enter the market because of the domination of the leading companies finally prompted action by the Office of Fair Trading (OFT). To determine 'whether there was a monopoly situation in the supply of artificial lower limbs in the UK, and, if so, whether any matters relating to that situation operated against the public interest', the Monopolies and Mergers Commission (MMC) was asked by the OFT on 9 December 1987 to look at this supremacy. A sample table on the facing page from a welter of statistics confronting the MMC serves as illustration.

Later figures from the OFT indicated that 62,000 people rely on artificial limbs, 80 per cent required lower limbs, and of these 75 per cent were believed to be of pensionable age. As the Director-General of the OFT, Sir Gordon Borrie, noted: 'to those who need artificial lower limbs it is important that their requirements are met as efficiently and cheaply as possible', so while the market might not be extraordinarily large – estimated to be worth around £37m per year – the 'widespread deficiencies' and limited competition found by Professor McColl were said to be critical.

The OFT was also concerned that 'the current purchasing and supply system appears to provide a strong disincentive for suppliers to increase efficiency or reduce costs, while profit levels within the industry appear to be high'. The progress on new contracts during the MMC investigation led Professor McColl to remark: 'I'm itching to get more competition in' (*Disability Now*, February 1988), and this is precisely what the MMC's document *Artificial*

InterMed table 1984					
	Hanger	*Vessa*	*Blatchford*	*Cossins*	*Stubbs*
No. of patients per contractor	28,528	11,097	9,134	844	903
% of all lower limb patients	50%	22%	18%	2%	2% [†]
% of new lower limb patients	42%	27%	25%	3%	3%
% of total orders in 1984 for new and replacement limbs	48%	25%	23%	2%	2%
% of total orders for repairs	56%	23%	17%	2%	2%

(*† figures as given*)

Lower Limbs prescribed. Presented to Parliament in April 1989, it decreed that although a monopoly situation as defined in Section 6(1)(a) of the Fair Trading Act 1973 existed in favour of Blatchfords, according to the MMC's calculations, the company had only 26 per cent of the market, certainly less than half. To most right-minded observers, the survey seemed uncommonly fair and just to the company. On the other hand, the MMC found that InterMed's conduct of its market domination was against the public interest and recommended that it should be divided by the divestment by October 1989 of either Hangers' or Vessa's shares, but neither company should be sold to Blatchfords. The Basingstoke company was exonerated from misconduct of its business and its 'history of negotiating responsibly and reasonably' recognised. The use of high-tech carbon fibre and alloys in components made Endolite more expensive than limbs using more conventional methods, and it was reckoned to be cost-effective in that limb-manufacturing time was reduced, and the proven durability of the limb left the incidence of repairs generally limited to the cosmesis and service items. Nevertheless, in spite of R&D expenditure and the quality of the product, the Commission's verdict that unit costs were too high needed to be looked at carefully.

Competitive Tendering

One of the DSA's first priorities in April 1988 had been to redraw contracts into a form suitable for individual contractors. The whole of the NHS was to be affected by the spirit of the enterprise culture, so the cost-plus format familiar to the industry was replaced by a series of three contracts as from 1 January 1989. One was for the provision of conventional limbs, a second for modular component parts, with another contract to govern the prosthetic services at centres. Before the services to patients at the centres could be put out to tender, it was necessary to establish precisely who could supply the component parts. A sense

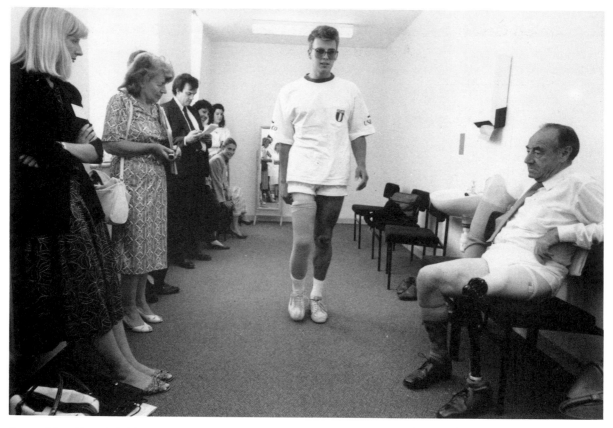

Stuart Metcalfe, a right above-knee amputee, demonstrates his walking ability to invited guests at the formal opening of the Blatchford Prosthetic Research Centre at Basingstoke District Hospital while a left above-knee patient, without a cosmesis on his Blatchford Endolite artificial leg, looks on.

of urgency in meeting the deadlines for the new contracts was communicated to the existing manufacturers who had tendered at the end of 1988 for this part of the business, and it was Blatchfords which emerged with a greater share of the component market than before.

Although sales were increasing greatly, high interest rates and the need to fund research from the company's own resources drastically slashed profit margins. A further aggravation was that under the structure of the new contracts,

payment came later than before and, with the company expanding so rapidly, when the DSA disassociated itself from an understanding made with the DHSS in 1985 for them to pay for the MAP stock in mid-1988, Blatchfords was left with a vast amount of stock which was not paid for. Cash flow staggered under this bodyblow, the company went into overdraft and in such circumstances running a stable business proved difficult. Of particular concern was the reported information that the company's conventional limbs were over 25 per cent more expensive than the nearest rival. To be competitive, therefore, limb prices had to be reduced by this amount. Whereas larger companies tend to be centrally controlled on policy matters from which they find it slow to diverge, Blatchfords

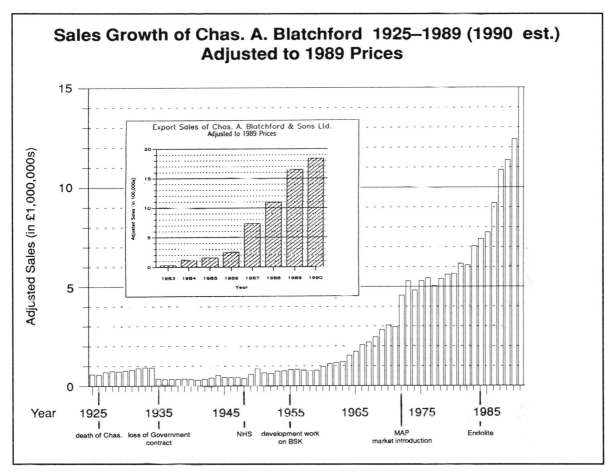

Sales Growth of Chas. A. Blatchford 1925–1989 (1990 est.)
Adjusted to 1989 Prices

Export Sales of Chas. A. Blatchford & Sons Ltd.
Adjusted to 1989 Prices

Adjusted Sales (in £1,000,000s)

Year: 1925 — death of Chas. / loss of Government contract; 1935; 1945 — NHS / development work on BSK; 1955; 1965; 1975 — MAP market introduction; 1985 — Endolite

was prepared to streamline and co-operate with the changing requirements of the DSA. Thus, with the collaboration of the shopfloor, an increased level of productivity ensured the mandatory price reductions were achieved, and the company won a greater share of the conventional limb business than they had before. Under Stephen's generalship, the strategy on tenders worked remarkably well, and when shortly afterwards the tender for Roehampton was conducted, once again the company's award was a bigger slice of the business.

The DSA by now had the information in place to encourage individual prosthetists to set up, and a concern of Blatchfords was to retain the same amount of prosthetic business as before to keep everyone employed. In the wake of the DHSS wish to phase out single-contractor centres, new contracts from the DSA for 1988 wanted Blatchfords to help supply the independent prosthetists and other contractors at Harold Wood, Bristol and Oxford. The DSA is known to favour localised manufacture of limbs, and the result of tendering in an extremely competitive manner is that, besides Newcastle, Stanmore and Roehampton, the DSA agreed to supply the company with nearly double the number of patients at other centres. Blatchfords also opened a new branch late in 1989 at Dulwich. This expansionist trend, however, was balanced by a drop-off in trading due to Departmental cut-backs in the provision of spare limbs for patients, and also by the fact that some of these extra patients failed to materialise.

How to retain the skills of prosthetists trained at the company's expense, with their instinctive feedback on minute details affecting individual patients, is one of the concerns for the 1990s. The potential loss of traditional standards of personal contact led Donald Castle-Smith, Chairman of the National Association of Limbless Disabled (NALD) to comment in *Disability Now* (February 1988) that 'The staff at centres need to be prepared to spend more time with each person.' Ken Chick, then Manager for Blatchfords at Roehampton, explained to *The Times* (9 February 1988) that the medical officer and prosthetist should discuss the prescription for each case, the prosthetist making a special point during the measurement and cast of the stump to gain the confidence of apprehensive patients. Every need should be catered for, and a limb provided which was strong, light, cosmetically acceptable and suitable for the patient's lifestyle. Knowing that they could not be hurt, children with these limbs loved kicking brick walls, so the limb had to be more than somewhat robust. Furthermore, Chick pointed out, for beach needs Blatchfords had a waterproof thermoplastic activity limb. To further these aims, since January 1986 the company has enjoyed the services of a research prosthetist taken on specifically to progress socket design and fitting, reinforced in 1988 by a second such specialist.

From 1 November 1985 Endolite components for Scotland were supplied to Robert Kellie, an InterMed subsidiary, based in a Dundee factory, with workshops at all the six limb-fitting centres and by far the largest supplier north of the

Tweed. Blatchfords had just the single workshop at the largest Scottish limb-fitting centre, The Belvidere Hospital in Glasgow. Significant inroads were made into the strong position held by Kellies when the contracts for prosthetic and related technical services operative from 1 January 1989 were put out to tender by the Common Services Agency for the Scottish Health Service. Kellies put in an offer in writing to supply, but refused to tender and suffered a crushing reverse. Blatchfords were offered two-thirds of the Glasgow work, twice as much as before, and Kellies nothing, leaving InterMed without representation at any Scottish centre. The company is well aware that it could end up with more conventional limbs than can currently be coped with, but the Scandinavian subsidiary, LIC (UK), and Rehabilitation Engineering Services – a Strathclyde University offshoot and consisting of ex-Kellie employees and a former prosthetist from Blatchfords – have entered Scotland and look serious contenders for future tender rounds. With the extra English business and these new notches in its Scottish belt, it became the Board's view that Blatchfords could turn out to be the largest single prosthetic company in England following the fragmentation caused by the new contracts, as the combined volume of work placed with Hangers and Vessa (now known jointly as Vessa) is smaller in size.

Exporting into the 1990s

More than Brian, Stephen shapes Board meetings to thrash things out and set in train a world-wide sales drive that has already met with success. Over 50,000 Endolite components

The British Design Award, 1990 certificate for the Endolite system.

British Design Award
1990

Presented to

Chas A Blatchford & Sons Limited

on 15 February 1990
at The Design Centre, London
to mark the selection of the

Endolite

designed by
Brian G Blatchford
John J Shorter
Victor J Woolnough

**BRITISH
DESIGN
AWARD
1990**

Sir Simon Hornby, Chairman

Ivor Owen, Director General

FACSIMILE

The Design Council, London

have been sold by Blatchfords and provided to patients in the form of limbs, primarily supplied through the DHSS. According to figures received from the DSA, Endolite above-knee sales in July 1988 were about 65 per cent of the total modular market and Endolite below-knee sales, 55 per cent. Three months later, the DSA intimated that the company should increase its entitlements to the modular market to 70 per cent and 65 per cent respectively. As uncertainties in the structure of prosthetic supply have increased, sole dependence on a single major customer in a highly volatile situation forced Blatchfords to adopt an ever more commercial outlook. Great interest in Endolite promotion has been generated with overseas consumers, signposted by the widening of John Shorter's role to the direction of marketing operations, and opportunities outside the UK are constantly under review. The evolving modifications of Endolite attracted wide attention in Europe and Japan, and an in-depth assessment of the Japanese market was looked at for the first time when a meeting with the Keiai Orthopaedic Appliance Company took place on 27 February 1987.

By May 1987 the Board had agreed that the mark should be registered in further countries. The export drive took on new impetus in 1987 when LIC and then Pi-Medica began to market Endolite throughout Scandinavia. Blatchfords gradually started to erode the Otto Bock grasp on several markets in the world. A telling break-through was television exposure at the Nuremberg Orthopaedic Show, when Greg Mannino, one of the first amputees to run leg-over-leg, chased up and down corridors during a five-minute slot. Nothing like it had been seen in Germany and soon the telephone was ringing. By November 1988 a distributor had been appointed in Germany, the first time a British company had succeeded in breaking into the Bock fiefdom – the lucrative, sensitive and influential German market.

Mannino was also videofilmed just three hours after being fitted with Endolite and was shown running, jumping and cycling with ease, causing this top American athlete to describe the limb as 'the prosthesis of tomorrow... the most phenomenal prosthesis on the market... function, flexion, everything about this leg is No. 1'. This powerful endorsement helped make the United States the company's biggest export customer, with a distribution team built around Alan Finnieston's company, AFI. On a visit to another centre in the USA Finnieston happened upon a chance Endolite leg leaning against a wall, doing nothing in particular. Picking it up and examining it with some wonderment, he asked those in earshot, 'Do you realise what you've got here?', and became an immediate convert. He had 140 people who wanted to go on the Endolite course, and export figures at the end of 1987 forecast a higher profit level, especially in North America.

Further good all-round results on the exporting front paved the way for a United Nations contract to equip a limb-fitting centre in Fuzhou. As part of the International Disability Services contract, three technicians from the Republic of China came to Basingstoke for training early in 1989. Despite Russian pressure on the British Government to provide limbs for the victims of the Armenian earthquake disaster, sadly for the company the Germans got there first.

Ideas first mooted in December 1987 happened to mention a possible Endolite II. Valuable data collection for the ongoing process of Endolite improvement continues with collation of information from the Blatchford Prosthetic Research Centre and from the company's 13 limb-fitting centres as well as international sources. The new Endolite represents the culmination of the company's latest R&D effort, planned to be launched in the

The Board of Directors: Stephen Blatchford (Managing Director), John Shorter (Technical & Marketing Director), Bill Blatchford (Chairman), Tony Rainbird (Financial Director and Company Secretary) and Joyce Blatchford.

middle of the centenary year. While it waits in the wings, the new decade was unveiled in the grand manner with news of a British Design Award for Endolite and further Royal recognition in the shape of the Queen's Award for Technological Achievement, both appropriate acknowledgement of over five years of intensive research and rigorous approval testing. The distinction of being the only medical product to win a British Design Award in 1990 sits happily with the unique triple gained in 1976 and the medals for excellence presented to Chas. in the Edwardian era, proof positive that the founder's philosophy of 'The patient comes first' has been clinched by successive family generations. Meanwhile, as a recent Board minute ends, 'Busy time for export and marketing…'.

Bibliography

Advanced Composites Engineering, Winter 1987.

Basingstoke Gazette, 9 April 1976.

Blatchford, B. S., and Shorter, J. J. *Chas. A. Blatchford & Sons Ltd. Technical Developments 1988*. (duplicated typescript).

Boast, Mary. *The Story of Bermondsey*. London Borough of Southwark, [1978]. (Neighbourhood Histories, No.5).

British Medical Journal.

Broca, A., and Ducroquet. *Artificial Limbs*. University of London Press, 1918.

Brooks, Stewart M. *Civil War Medicine*. Springfield, Illinois: Charles Thomas, [1966].

Civilian Health and Medical Services; edited by Sir Arthur MacNalty. Vol.II. HMSO, 1955.

Disabled Soldier's Handbook. Ministry of Pensions, 1918.

Disability Now, February 1988.

Fliegel, O., and Feuer, S. G. *Historical Development of Lower-Extremity Prostheses*; from *Archives of Physical Medicine & Rehabilitation*, 47, 1966.

Gower, E. S. compiler. *Queen Mary's Hospital, Roehampton: General Hospital and Limb Fitting Centre*. [c.1966]. (outline duplicated typescript history).

Gray, Frederick. *Automatic Mechanism, as applied in the Construction of Artificial Limbs, in cases of amputation*. H. Renshaw, 1855.

Great Britain. Army Medical Department. *Medical and Surgical History of the British Army which served in Turkey and Crimea*. 2 vols. Harrison, 1858.

Great Britain. Ministry of Pensions. *Artificial Limbs and their Relation to Amputations*. HMSO, 1939.

Hampshire Business Gazette, April 1988.

Judge, G. *Survey of Knee Mechanisms for Artificial Limbs*. Rev.ed. BRADU, 1980. (duplicated typescript).

Lancet, The.

Little, E. Muirhead. *Artificial Limbs and Amputation Stumps*. H. K. Lewis, 1922.

London and Provincial Medical Directory. 1847.

Medical Directory. annual.

Monopolies and Mergers Commission. *Artificial Lower Limbs: a Report on the supply of artificial lower limbs in the United Kingdom*. HMSO, [1989]. (Cm. 594).

Otis, George A. , and Huntingdon, D. L. *The Medical and Surgical History of the War of the Rebellion*. Vol.II. Surgical History. 1876–83.

Post Office London Directory. annual.

Putti, Vittorio. *Historic Artificial Limbs*. New York: Hoebner, 1930.

Queen's Gift Book in aid of Queen Mary's Convalescent Auxiliary Hospitals... Hodder and Stoughton, [1917]. (with illustrated inset).

Review of the Artificial Limb and Appliance Centre Services. 2 vols. HMSO, 1986. ('The McColl Report').

Rubber Developments, October 1987.

Shorter, J. J. *Endolite – The High Technology prosthesis.* ISPO, Belgium, 15 November 1986. (duplicated typescript).

Therapy Weekly, 6 February 1986.

Thomas, S., *and others. Leather Manufacture through the Ages.* Proceedings of the 27th East Midlands Industrial Archaeology Conference, 1983.

Thompson, Roy S. *Leather Manufacture in the post-medieval period with special reference to Northamptonshire;* from *Post-Medieval Archaeology,* 15, 1981.

Thompson, Roy S. *Tanning: Man's first manufacturing process?;* from Newcomen Society for the study of the history of Engineering and Technology. *Transactions,* vol. 53, 1981–2.

War Medicine, 1, 1941.

White's Devon Directory. 1850.

Video: Chas. A. Blatchford & Sons Ltd. *One Step Ahead.* Braham Hill Ltd. [1987].

Index

Figures in italics refer to picture captions